ADVANCE PRAISE FOR CHAMPION MINDSET

"This book is as powerful as it is seemingly simple. And more importantly, it is real. I know because I have been a client of Service Champions for years. You are going to enjoy what Kevin has done here, take it to heart."

Patrick Lencioni,
Best-selling Author, *The Ideal Team Player*

"I've seen firsthand how this business helped shape the lives of many people. Kevin has always put people first, developing a culture that led to growing an incredibly successful business."

Joe Cristiano, former CEO and President,
Kelly-Moore Paint Company and
Chairman of the Board, Bank of San Francisco

"A quick read (thank you, Kevin), Comerford details how he made the critical transition from an entrepreneurial-driven firm to one that is professional-led without losing the entrepreneurial spirit. It's a tricky transition, and Kevin does a brilliant job of illuminating the mindset and values that make it possible."

Verne Harnish, Founder,
Entrepreneurs' Organization (EO) and
author of *Scaling Up (Rockefeller Habits 2.0)*

"In Champion Mindset, Kevin Comerford reveals the attitudes and skills that will give you a competitive advantage. He reminds us that champions aren't born. They're made. Kevin's passion for leadership and

service shines through in the values that have made his company a success. This book will give you the tools to think like a champion."

Carmine Gallo, Communication Coach
and Best-selling Author of ten books,
including *The Apple Experience* and *Talk Like TED*

"Kevin has built a company that performs at a high level when it comes to client satisfaction, culture, people development and profitability. He's packaged it all up and built one of the finest companies in the industry."

Ken Haines, CEO, Wrench Group, LLC

"The relationships that Kevin has built are extraordinary. This book gives you tips on how to create those relationships inside of an organization. We have worked with the team at Service Champions throughout the years, and they truly are leaders and have a culture that is second to none."

Darren Hicks, Retired Navy SEAL,
Owner/CEO, Hicks Professional Group

"Champion Mindset is a must-read for any entrepreneur, business owner, or leader who needs a blueprint for success. Learning, embracing, and practicing a set of core values, which drives its culture, is at the heart of America, as well as its most successful businesses. Kevin, and his real-life company, Service Champions, is no exception. Kevin has created a unique company, with explosive growth, that is an icon and envy within the service industry, demonstrating the principles in this book at work. Packed with valuable nuggets and take-aways, you'll enjoy following Emily, the main character, as she navigates through these life-changing lessons."

Paul Kelly, Southwestern CEO of the Wrench Group...
and CEO of Parker & Sons Heating,
AC, Plumbing and Electrical

"The book is fantastic. Each chapter has great life lessons in areas of management, leadership, and personal well-being. The principles in this book can be applied to any business."

Greg Reid, Best-selling Author,
Entrepreneur, Speaker, Filmmaker

"Champion Mindset is an excellent read for anyone looking to improve their leadership or their company. Kevin uses great stories to educate us on Champion's core values and how they provide guiding principles for his leaders and employees. These core values build confidence in his team to make high quality decisions for the employees, customers, and the business. This fosters a culture where his employees get excited about delivering remarkable customer service, which is key in creating Champion's competitive advantage in the market."

Mike Hart, Vice President,
Residential Sales, Lennox International

"Kevin is a unicorn for small businesses. There are very few or any like him. They have had consistent, explosive growth year after year, all fueled by Kevin's passion and enthusiasm."

Mark Berch, Founder and President,
Service Finance Company

"An easy-read parable that tells the story of a company and how leadership and core values make all the difference. This parable is about turning an ordinary business into an extraordinary one by adopting a highly differentiated mindset. It's an incredibly good message that a mundane, undifferentiated business can be put on steroids with a turbo'ed mindset."

Frank Slootman, CEO & Founder, Snowflake

BUILDING GREATNESS BY HAVING THE
RIGHT PHILOSOPHY AND VALUES

CHAMPION
MINDSET

KEVIN
COMERFORD

CHAMPION MINDSET
Building Greatness by Having the
Right Philosophy and Values
Kevin Comerford

Copyright ©2021

ISBN: 978-1-7351657-6-9

Joint Venture Publishing
Blue Sky R&D, LLC

This is a work of fiction. Names, characters, places, and incidents are the products of the author's imagination or are used fictitiously. Any resemblance to actual events, locales, or persons, living or dead, is entirely coincidental.

Printed in the United States of America

ACKNOWLEDGEMENTS

What a life I've had, and there have been so many people who have helped me along the way.

<u>To my family</u>: I'm blessed with the best homefield advantage anyone could ask for. My beautiful wife and grammar queen, Carolyn, I love you very much, and I'm so thankful I get to spend the rest of my years with you. My children, Emily, Brendan, and Landon, I am so proud of all three of you. You have been great kids from the day you were born, and each year our relationship keeps getting better. I thank God every day for putting you in my life.

<u>To my parents</u>: Mom and Dad, you have helped and guided me in life and business. I learned so much from you, and I am truly grateful. The values that lead Service Champions were the values I saw you live every day at home and work. I love you!

<u>To my sister and brother-in-law</u>: Thank you, Leanne and Matt. You have always been there for me. I love you very much.

<u>To my mentors</u>:

<u>Joe Cristiano</u>: You have been an incredible teacher, mentor, and friend for 30 years. You have been such a positive influence on my business and my life. I love you and your beautiful bride, Janet,

very much. There are no words to describe the appreciation I have for you.

Ron McCann: You took me in when I was new in this business and nurtured me into the leader I am today. You encouraged me with your words to become a great student. Thank you, brother.

Leland Smith: Wow! What a successful run we had building two businesses together. Thank you, Leland, for your continuous guidance and counsel for 17 spectacular years. I'll never forget our weekly calls.

Ron Huntington: As our coach, you've helped guide our business to greatness and kept us on track. As a friend, you've helped my family and me with your mentorship and love.

To Ray Dias: The closest thing to a brother I've had. For over 25 years, your support and loyalty have been unwavering. You have meant so much to me and my family, and you have been the glue that has kept Service Champions together for 18 years.

To Cookie Silva: Thank you for the dedication and spirit you have brought every single day. I'm so proud to call you a founder of this beautiful business. You're the best, dude!

To Erin Glass: You have been fantastic and so steadfast in your support and protection of me. I am so thankful for all the years we've worked side by side. There were so many times you made this book come alive with your ideas or your accountability in bringing it to a close.

To our Service Champions Team: What a team I've been blessed with! This book is about your success and all you do every day to take care of each other and our wonderful clients.

To my best buddies: Chris Connolly, Peter Gaeckle, Don Garman, Pace Linck, Scott Mamola, Matthew Toombs (nephew), your constant encouragement and belief in me is humbling and appreciated. Thank you for pushing me to always be better.

To my Families Mastermind Group: What a special group we had for many years. It was life changing in so many ways. Thank you, Mark Aitken, John Akohian, Gus Antos, Jonathan Bancroft, Steve Burbridge, Dave Geiger, and Leland Smith.

To Dan Sullivan: Founder and CEO of Strategic Coach®, I have followed and "surrendered" to your teachings since 1996. You have changed my life and had such a positive impact on my family.

To Verne Harnish: Founder and CEO of Gazelles, Inc., when my company was "stuck," your book *(Mastering the Rockefeller Habits)* and organization provided a structure that accelerated our 20%+ growth year after year.

TABLE OF CONTENTS

INTRODUCTION

 For many years, I've been accused of being too optimistic and have been told I need to be more of a "realist." I have no idea what a "realist" is; I guess I hope I never become one. Sure, there are days when I have "stinkin' thinkin'" going on and I need a checkup from the neck up. What I've learned is that having the right mindset is what makes the difference. When it comes to having the right mindset, it takes daily effort to keep a positive attitude. Every morning at 5:00 a.m., you will find me reflecting, in writing, on my 3-5 wins from the previous day. This discipline or habit keeps me focused on what went well from the previous day. It frees my mind of any negativity that may look to creep in. This exercise for the mind gives me energy, builds confidence, gives me a sense of gratitude, and prepares me to attack today with rigor and enthusiasm.

The next step in the daily ritual is using the fuel of achievement from the previous day to help set 3-5 goals (wins) for today. This is where having the right personal philosophy is so important. The philosophy I live my life by is: "Always make your future bigger than your past." This is a philosophy built on living a life of continuous growth. It shows up everywhere in my life and has become a thought habit that is supported by my words and actions. At the end of all my relevant emails, texts, and letters, rather than "sincerely," the closing I use is, "Here's to a Bigger Future." So when I'm setting my 3-5 goals for today, I'm always looking at how I can become better and grow more today.

This continuous looking back on what I accomplished and looking forward to the exciting things the future holds has been a formula for success in my life. *Champion Mindset* dives into both mindset and philosophy in great detail and will give you a road map to stay on the right path along your success journey.

* * * *

I grew up in a small town called Pleasanton, which is a suburb of San Francisco. The street I grew up on was nicknamed "Chicken Alley." That's because it was normal to see chickens crossing the street and people riding horses along this country road. My mentor, Joe, who is one of the lead characters in this book, always told me to remember where I came from and, no matter how successful I became, it all started on Chicken Alley. What Joe was telling me was to stay humble, even when you're being portrayed as a mastermind, genius, or bigger-than-life success. Like so many other bits of knowledge and gifts Joe shared, he was once again right. Humility has played a huge role in my development as a leader. It's about never taking myself too seriously and always remembering that I need people and a great team around me to be successful. Humility is one of the core attributes of maintaining a champion mindset. Being a lifelong student, even when I've achieved incredible success, has been a key reason why my company and personal life continue to skyrocket to new heights.

This book is about a character named Emily and the struggles she goes through on her journey in this make-believe company, Champion Air Conditioning.

Emily learns from the team members what it takes to be successful and how humility is something she will have to tap into quite often, especially when she experiences success.

She is also introduced to the company's core values, which are the foundational pillars that make up Champion's culture.

Culture is defined as the attitudes and behaviors of the team members that make up the company. Emily sees firsthand those core values come alive as the team members interact with each other and their clients.

Emily also learns the company's philosophy and how, by applying it daily, she can overcome any challenge or obstacle she faces.

I'm delighted you have chosen to read or listen to this book. I'm certain it will make a difference in your life.

Keep in mind, as you begin to experience phenomenal success, always stay humble and remember where you came from. So, Joe, here's to Chicken Alley and never forgetting where it all started.

Here's to a Bigger Future,

Kevin Comerford

1

THE FIRST DAY

 Everything was new to Emily on the first day of her job at Champion Air Conditioning. She was grateful for the job and the fact that they were willing to train inexperienced new hires. At the age of 18 and fresh out of high school, her interest level in traditional careers was low, and she hoped this opportunity would spark a career aspiration, while providing her with job skills she could use in the future.

She hesitantly walked through the door, where she approached a few team members who were topping off their coffee cups and looking over their service orders for the day.

"Can I help you?" a middle-aged man asked.

"Yes, I'm Emily, and this is my first day. Can you tell me where I'm supposed to go?" she replied.

"It's good to meet you, Emily," said another man. "I'm Joe. I think Sarah has some payroll forms for you to fill out," he said pointing to a door across the room. "If you have any questions, she'll be happy to help you."

"Thank you," the new service technician smiled.

As the CEO of Champion Air Conditioning, Joe often spent time with his team members as the day got started. He used a technique called MBWA, "Management By Wandering Around." He did this so he could make great connections and also get a feel for how the operation was running. On this particular day, Joe was in the support center. He was within eye and earshot of Sarah's office, so he could hear the exchange with the new recruit.

"Welcome to Champion, Emily!" Sarah said in the friendly tone she used with everyone who approached her. Always helpful, Sarah was an asset to Joe and the company. As one of the first people to encounter new team members, she represented the company well.

"Thank you so much. I'm excited to be here," said Emily.

"Great. Tell me, what makes you excited to be here?" asked Sarah.

"Well, when I heard about the opportunity, I visited your website, and the first thing that caught my eye was the slogan of your training university—"A High-Paying Career, Without a Four Year." Most of my friends will be starting college at the end of summer, and they'll be there for four years. I really liked the idea that I might be able to attend Champions University and finish in weeks, rather than years," Emily remarked.

"Ah yes, Champions University is designed to provide you with the skills you'll need in less time than the typical university," Sarah said, "but make no mistake, you'll receive a real education, one that's rigorous. You'll definitely walk out ready to put your skills to work."

"That's just what I'm looking for!" Emily said, suddenly noticing a sign on the wall. "Hey, those are the same Core Values I read on your website, right?"

★ CORE VALUES ★

1. GIVE REMARKABLE SERVICE

Every interaction will leave a mark. Make it positive and memorable, so much so that the client will remark to their friends and family. Wow the client with your actions and solutions-based approach.

2. DRIVE TOP PERFORMANCE

We expect excellence from ourselves, just as our clients expect it from us. We measure results and reward those who deliver. The ultimate goal is a lasting relationship.

3. HONOR OUR COMMITMENTS

We follow through with what we say we're going to do; this behavior is critical in building trust.

4. BE A LIFE-LONG STUDENT

Be open to learning and new possibilities. Continue to challenge yourself and get outside your comfort zone.

5. HAVE FUN & ENJOY THE MOMENT

Be present and in the Now. Life is short, life is precious. Be happy with what is going right. Focus on progress, measure backwards.

6. BE KIND & ENCOURAGING

We genuinely care for others and their overall well-being. We are great listeners and we use our words to inspire and build people up.

TRUSTWORTHY ★ ON-TIME ★ WORRY-FREE

"They sure are! Get used to seeing them, too, because you'll find them everywhere, in the breakroom, the conference room, the call center, and the warehouse. Before long, you'll know them like the back of your hand."

"Interesting. So they really mean something?"

"Oh, very much so. Everyone at Champion lives and works by those core values in everything they do. I know I do!" Sarah smiled.

"The more I hear, the more I think I'm really going to like working here!" Emily said enthusiastically.

"That's great. We're all happy to have you aboard. And that said, now that you've signed these forms, you're ready to start your day. Let me see who you're supposed to be with today," she said.

Hearing that, Joe stepped forward. He had listened to parts of their conversation and was impressed that the new service technician had taken the initiative to visit and read the website. She wanted to know more about the company, and it seemed that the major benefits of being a team member at Champion greatly appealed to her. These were qualities that caught his attention and made a good first impression. He found he wanted to know a little more about her and personally share with her a little more about the company he had formed.

"Thanks, Sarah. I'll take it from here," he said. "Emily, before you begin your day, I'm on my way to meet with some of our team members, and I'd like you to join me. Does that sound okay?"

"It sure does!" Emily answered, excited to go on the tour with Joe.

She thought he might work for Sarah in the People Department, so she asked, "What do you do here, Joe?"

"I work for everyone out here on the floor and throughout the company. My job is to make sure everyone is taken care of so they can perform to the best of their ability."

Still a little confused, she prodded a bit further, "Do you work for Sarah?"

"Absolutely. I'm the CEO here at Champion, and I work for the entire team."

It took Emily a minute to really process what Joe said. When she finally realized who her tour guide was, she was hit with a wave of nervousness and excitement, and a little disbelief.

Emily had never met a CEO before, and although she was a little nervous, she'd seen Shark Tank, so the thought of learning about mergers and acquisitions and big strategic decisions got her excited … and that's what she thought she was in for.

Joe could sense Emily's anxiousness, so he began their journey together with some simple open-ended conversation.

"So, Emily, tell me about yourself," said Joe.

"Well, I just graduated from high school a couple weeks ago. I live at home with my parents and two brothers."

"Congratulations on your graduation. What sports or activities were you involved in at school?"

"Actually, I was captain of the cheer team," Emily smiled, as she began to feel more confident. "It was a lot of fun, most of the time, anyway, except when I was on the bottom of the pyramid."

"I bet," Joe laughed. "Captain, huh? That's quite an accomplishment. Sounds like you had a lot of friends and a great social experience in high school. Tell me about that."

"Sure, I had friends. I was the girl that wanted to get along with everybody. It was challenging at times because I had different interests. So many of my friends were into partying and getting drunk. I really wanted people to like me, so at first, I started doing that stuff. After a while, I realized if I kept that up, I'd end up flunking out and going nowhere. When those 'friends' saw that I was looking to make more of my life than partying, they stopped calling me, stopped inviting me to parties. It was really hard, and there were times I felt all alone."

"Wow, Emily, you really are a strong young lady. When you were sharing that story, it reminded me of a quote by Abraham Lincoln: 'If you want to lead the orchestra, you have to turn your back on the crowd.' What he was saying there is exactly what you were experiencing with your friends. The decision you made to stop partying and getting drunk all the time was turning your back on the crowd. That allowed you to have a clear head and start your journey in becoming a leader. Being a leader can be lonely at times; you'll find it's the most rewarding thing you can do in life, both emotionally and financially. You mentioned you had different interests than your friends, what were they?"

"Well, don't laugh, I like to read, and I really enjoy listening to audio books," Emily answered.

"Laugh? Emily, that's fantastic. What kind of books? Drama? Or do you like a good true crime or mystery?"

"Well, I actually prefer to read biographies and autobiographies. I love to learn about people's journeys in life, the struggles they've had and how they persevered to keep moving forward, and their successes along the way. Those books inspire me."

"I'm impressed. I love to hear that from someone your age. It is so important when you're first starting out in business to read all of the books you can that inspire you. Make it a habit every day to read at least 10 pages of a good book that expands your learning. When you create this habit, you'll build a foundation of success that you'll tap into for your entire career. Emily, I've learned that readers are leaders. Those that take the time to develop themselves through reading tend to be the ones that lead others and organizations."

"Joe, it sounds like I'll be reading a lot about air conditioning. That's probably going to be the best thing for me to do to be a great technician."

"Well, Emily, that is important, and it is one of the ways to learn the technical side of the job. You'll find that 50 percent of your job is learning the technical skills of the trade. There's much more to this trade than technical skills."

"Like what?" Emily asked.

"We're in the service industry, or better yet, the people business. Most of our competitors think we're in the heating and air conditioning business. The reality, Emily, is we are in the emotions and experience business and the other 50 percent of your job will be learning communication skills so you'll be able to win over the client. I'll leave it there for now," Joe answered.

A puzzled look crossed Emily's face as she processed what Joe had said about 50 percent of her job being the technical skills and 50 percent of it being communication skills. All along, she had thought that to be a great technician she had to focus on her technical skills in order to fix air conditioners.

Just then, Joe commented, "Let's head to the warehouse and talk to the team out there."

Coming back into focus, Emily nodded in agreement as she followed Joe toward the back door.

They entered the pristine and neatly organized warehouse. It was huge with tall ceilings that went up to the roof and long aisles of shelves with parts stacked like cords of wood. Several men and women moved briskly, setting air conditioners in place to be picked up for today's jobs.

They walked along patiently, stopping to greet each of the team members along the way. Emily was completely dumbfounded as she observed Joe carrying on five-to-ten-minute conversations with each of the members. He knew all of them by name and also knew a little something about them and their family. What struck her more than anything was watching Joe truly connect with each person. Nothing else mattered in the world when he was engaged in a conversation.

"How's your son, Emanuel, doing at school? It's been about six months that he's been in Miami at college."

"What are you installing today, John? How's your wife, Marie? Did she finish her cooking classes?"

"Hey, Scott, is your boy still training to be a boxer?"

They must have met with ten technicians and warehouse staff. Emily was amazed as Joe made a deep connection with each of the people in his company. She noticed his ability to ask questions and stay focused and present with each person. He was interested in them, and the fact that he was the CEO of the company meant nothing.

The workers were also deeply engaged. It was amazing to watch—the more Joe was focused and present, the more they followed suit and were the same way.

About an hour later, they began to head back to Joe's office. Emily followed Joe and was still a bit punch drunk from the whole experience. When they arrived back to his office, Joe opened the journal he had been carrying and added more to his notes. The notes were on Marie finishing her cooking classes and Scott's son continuing to train for his first boxing match, which was coming up in two months, etc.

"Emily, I'm known in my company as someone who has an incredible memory. Here's my secret," Joe said and winked. "I've learned over the years that it's about the people. They matter the most. People don't care how much you know until they know how much you care. My job as the CEO is, first and foremost, to show my people, through my actions, that I care for them, that I love them like a brother or sister."

"So, Emily, what did you learn on our visit to the warehouse?" he asked.

"Joe," Emily said. "I have to tell you, I thought you were going to teach me about mergers and acquisitions and new product launches, and we might be visiting with executives in a mahogany boardroom. What I just saw blew my mind. Actually, I'm stunned. You took the time to be with each of your people, Joe. It seemed like nothing else mattered in the world. You were so focused and so engaged. I was impressed by the fact that you made everyone feel important, and it was totally genuine."

"I also noticed that all you did was ask questions of your team and let them share with you what's going on in their lives. They were excited to share, and you let them go on and on and stayed focused the entire time," she added.

"Very observant, Emily! Great leaders that I modeled myself after ask all the right questions, rather than thinking they have to have all the right answers. Every day I'm out here visiting with the team, I'm asking question after question. Some of the questions are about the business, while others are personal. I work daily to build trust with the staff so they feel safe in sharing with me where our issues are and how we can improve as a company.

"Emily, this is exactly what I want you to do with our clients. I want you to give them your undivided attention. I want you to be totally focused and engaged when you're in their home. That means being great at asking open-ended questions and being a great listener. Make them feel like they are the only client we are serving today. Our business has grown dramatically because we live by the belief that 'the smaller they think we are, the larger we will get.' Emily, as we talked about earlier, you have to be great at the technical skills of the trade; what I want you to understand is that our clients will remember how you made them feel versus what you did or said."

Joe shared stories about his early days and how he came to realize that the key to business success wasn't understanding financial statements and learning about mergers and acquisitions; it was about relationships and taking care of the people who took care of his company and his clients every day. Above all, it was about serving others with honesty and integrity.

"Honesty will get you far. So be authentic and choose to tell the truth, and your stress levels will decrease significantly. My mentor taught me that if you tell the truth at 10:00 in the morning, you won't have to worry about what you say at 2:00 in the afternoon," Joe said.

"I never thought of it that way," Emily admitted. "I bet your customers really appreciate that about your company."

"I have faith they do. Let me point out, though, that we call them clients. A customer is someone who does something once. A client is someone you have a relationship with. That's what we want with each and every client.

"Now, let's see, Emily, I'm going to have Sarah show you around the rest of our company and introduce you to our team of service technicians. And tomorrow, I think we'll get you started working with Washington. He's doing an equipment install and could use an extra hand. Besides that, I think you'll find he's an excellent teacher. I'll tell you what, come see me when you two are done and we'll talk some more," Joe offered.

"Really? You want me to come see you again? Do you think you'll be busy?"

"Emily, like everyone here at Champion, we all have a lot going on. I make time for the important things, and nothing is more important than spending time with team members like you. I've seen a ton of leaders of companies who lock themselves up in their office and focus on their to-do list and busy work. They totally cut themselves off from their people, and, in turn, they leave tons of money on the table. Whereas if they had just spent quality time with their people, they would capture so much more business and grow like crazy.

"Besides, Emily, I like your spirit, and you ask good questions," Joe answered. "I think you've got what it takes, Emily. I think you've got a champion mindset."

2

BEING WHETHER-DRIVEN

Emily found that Joe was right. Washington was patient and a great teacher. He took the time to explain the details of the air conditioning installation they completed and had a knack for explaining foreign, technical information so it was easy to understand.

It was obvious to Emily that she had much to learn, and Washington put her mind at ease, letting her know that learning takes time and what's most important is that she is present and engaged during her training process. He encouraged her to refrain from putting too much pressure on herself to learn everything now, telling her that with all the information she is going to be getting, it will feel like she's drinking water from a firehose. He encouraged her to trust the process and trust herself. Washington introduced her to a simple tool, that was created by Dan Sullivan, called The Positive Focus® as a way to help her consume all she was learning and to protect her confidence. At the end of each day, he had Emily take 10-15 minutes to write down the top 5 things she accomplished. Once she wrote down her accomplishments, she would then indicate why they were important. Next, she wrote the further progress she wanted to make on each accomplishment; then finally, she wrote the first action she would take on each one.

She completed this form every day during her training, and she found that it did exactly what Washington told her. It helped her quantify all that she was learning, while at the same time, it protected her confidence.

After completing the installation and demonstrating its key features to the homeowner, Washington and Emily returned to Champion.

"Emily, let's go to the break room and grab something to drink while I complete the paperwork," Washington suggested.

As Washington updated the client's file, Emily looked around the break room, otherwise known as "The HUB." It was bursting with activity—there were team members collaborating at the round tables, a fun game of ping pong going on in the corner, and the large island in the center of the room supplied healthy snacks and beverages for whomever chose to partake. It was a spacious, clean, pleasant, vibrant area, and Emily felt invigorated just looking around at the bold, colorful walls and the TV mounted high on a wall that displayed the latest company highlights.

She was surprised to find that someone had taken the time to make sure it was a clean and pleasant environment for the team members. Along with the typical refrigerator, microwave, and coffee pot, the room boasted a few plants and posters. What caught Emily's eye the most was a banner that spanned a large portion of the wall that read: BE WHETHER-DRIVEN.

"Hey, Washington, is that banner misspelled? Isn't it supposed to be *weather*? W E A T H E R," she asked, as she spelled it out.

"I can see why you'd think so, being that we provide heating and cooling to our clients," Washington commented. "Actually, it's spelled right."

"Really? Can you explain it to me?"

"Here at Champion, we're whether-driven," he said, spelling out the word. "Being WHETHER-driven is the core philosophy of our business. It's based on the belief that none of us will ever use the weather as a reason for our success or an excuse for our struggles when it comes to performance. At Champion, my success depends on WHETHER I come to work with the right attitude, and WHETHER I follow the Champion process, something we call 'Run the Play.'

"You see, Emily, at Champion we focus on what we can control. Our attitude is totally in our control, and it's a choice we make every day and throughout the day. We'll teach you a few techniques, like The Positive Focus, that you can use to help keep a positive attitude. Ultimately, it's up to you how you choose to look at situations that happen. I'm a believer that success is 10 percent about what happens to me and 90 percent about how I react to what happens to me. I've learned that everyone has the same challenges they are faced with in life. At some point, we're all going to deal with relationship challenges, financial challenges, and health challenges. It's how I respond to those challenges and the actions I take to make them better and see them through that makes all the difference."

"Wow, so just knowing that we're all going to face the same challenges allows me to feel less like a victim and more in control of my own destiny. I thought those things were only happening to me. It's liberating to hear that we're all faced with these issues and that how I respond makes all the difference."

"The second part of that statement is equally important. You have a choice every day whether you follow our proven process for success. The method we teach here at Champion is unique, and we're very detailed on the words we want you to use and the action we want you to take on each call. The more exact and precise you are on the process, or 'Running the Play,' the more success you will have. Like a football team, we practice running the play over and over again in Champions University, and then once you're out on your own, we come back weekly and practice during our training classes."

"I'll definitely make every effort to "Run the Play" on every call."

"That's great to hear. Remember that when you're struggling or going through some challenging times. Sticking to the process and going back to basics is easy to do. I will tell you, it's easier not to do. What I've seen sometimes is technicians want to create their own process or take shortcuts on the process we have created. That can get you into trouble and make for some inconsistent results, which can cause frustration."

"Wait, weather is important in this business, correct?" Emily asked.

"Some might see it that way. And it's probably true for a lot of companies. Weather is what drives their business. If our business was centered around the weather, we'd be like everyone else, struggling to grow, laying off people in between seasons, and relying on something we have no control over," Washington replied.

"I'm still confused," Emily commented.

"Well, let's say it's 100 degrees outside, Emily. When that happens, it's probably pretty easy to sell air conditioning systems, isn't it?"

"Sure, people would be really uncomfortable!" she agreed.

"That's right. They'll buy an air conditioning system or hire a company to repair their existing one without blinking an eye. The weather is driving their decision and getting cooling now is more important than thinking about which company to choose."

"I can imagine. Doesn't that mean you should be *weather* driven?" she asked.

"One would think, right? What we've found is that the opposite is true," he posed. "Let me explain. If a company builds their business around this scenario, what happens when the temperature drops and it's mild outside?"

"People probably wouldn't be looking to buy a new air conditioner, or fix their old one, right?"

"That's right, our sales would drop, and our service department would have no work. We figured out years ago that we cannot control the weather, so we focus on what we can control, which is our mindset and following the Champion process. While most people wait for Mother Nature to create business and drive sales, at Champion, we create business no matter what the weather's like," advised Washington.

"Let me give you another example that I see happen every year. Let's say it's 72 degrees outside, and HVAC contractors and vendors everywhere are complaining about the lack of work. Do we listen to their complaining and let it paralyze us and affect our attitude—and then use it as an excuse for our lack of performance? Or do we tune out what the crowd is saying and go to work on the things we do have control over?"

"I would think that if other companies and vendors are struggling, we would be struggling, too?" Emily questioned.

"That's where we're different," Washington stated confidently. "99.9 percent of the challenges we face are internal, meaning they are inside our own minds and, therefore, inside our company. If we go to work and win the battles in our own mind every day, and we look to be positive and take action to create business, rather than waiting for it to come, we will overcome any of the external challenges we face.

"There are two key actions we take when the weather gets mild. First, we take a very proactive approach in marketing and calling our clients outbound. That action is in our control, and we've built our company around this philosophy.

"Number two is slowing down and being thorough. Our company stays disciplined in limiting the number of calls that a tech runs every day. We do that so the techs can spend quality time with the client and can be thorough in assessing all of the client's home comfort needs. It's easy to shy away from this when we're in a heat wave and the phones are ringing off the hook. Keeping disciplined to the belief that less is more increases our client satisfaction and the revenues on the calls we run. At Champion, we believe that time equals love."

"Okay, so I'm confused now. I've heard that time equals money before. How does time equal love?" she asked.

"Let me see if I can explain it this way. If you asked a young toddler what the definition of love is, do you think they would be able to tell you?"

"Likely, no."

"I agree. The only way a young child understands love and gets the sense that you care for them is if you spend time with and are fully engaged with them. Turning off your phone and getting rid of all other distractions, then you can be fully present—that is how you show them love and care.

"The same is true with our clients," Washington continued. "By slowing down and spending quality time with them, they will know we love and care for them. We call that being thorough on each call."

"Oh, I get it. The more time you spend with them, the more they know you care about them, right?"

"You got it, Emily. Imagine how discouraged we'd all be if we waited for the weather to generate business! Being whether-driven helps our company thrive, and it has a tremendous impact on everyone's attitude," he added.

"I think I struggle sometimes with allowing other people to affect my attitude," Emily admitted.

"That's very normal, and you're definitely part of the majority. It's easy to get sucked into other people's negativity and complaining. That's what Joe means when he says we need to be different. Be the person who brings optimism and hope to conversations, relationships, and interactions. Be the sunshine and light for others in a world that can be dark. It's the difference between having an abundancy mentality versus a scarcity mentality."

"Can you explain that to me?" she asked.

"There are two different mindsets you can live your life by: Abundancy or Scarcity.

"Abundancy allows us to turn weaknesses into opportunities and transform negative experiences into positive ones. People with abundancy mindsets are grateful for what they have. They are creative and cooperative and see all of the opportunities life has to offer. They believe that there is plenty for all of us to go around and there is no need to hoard or hold onto what they have or know. Abundant people share openly and freely. They believe that *givers gain.*

"Scarcity is just the opposite. People with a scarcity mindset believe that everything necessary for future progress is becoming scarce and running out. They believe that if someone does well, it must be at the expense of everyone else who is doing poorly. They think that once resources are depleted, they are gone forever; therefore, you must compete to get as many resources as possible, while restricting them from others."

"Okay, I think I understand the differences between the two. How will I know if I'm living a life that is abundant or scarce?"

"That's a great question, Emily. Our feelings operate as indicators, or a dashboard that you would see on a car. Pay attention to how you're feeling, and that will tell you which mindset you're living. An abundancy mindset leaves you feeling excited, motivated, and energized for action. A scarcity mindset leaves you feeling overwhelmed, depressed, and paralyzed. Scarcity is filled with envy, guilt, and anger."

"Wow, so it's my feelings I need to pay attention to. I got it! How do these mindsets apply or show up every day at Champion?"

"I'll go back to our core philosophy here at Champion—Whether-driven, to best explain how this applies. Working inside a heating and cooling company, it's easy to fall into the trap that we need weather to be successful. This shows up by allowing the weather report to influence how a salesperson or technician feels or how they see the day. Someone with a scarcity mindset sees the fog rolling in over the hills on a June day, and it sets them back mentally. When the fog rolls in, Emily, it's going to be a mild 75-degree day. A scarcity mindset allows things outside of our control, the weather, to affect us. Sales performance suffers because of the choice made to adopt that mindset."

"I have to tell you, Washington, I can see how it's easy to fall into that trap. How do I guard against that?"

"It's easy to adopt an abundancy mindset. It's easier not to do, though, Emily. It starts with awareness, like I shared earlier – paying attention to the feeling indicators. Then being intentional about creating the habit of looking at all situations from the perspective of abundance. So let's go back and talk about that situation with the fog rolling in and knowing it's going to be a mild day. The person with an abundancy mindset sees the opportunity in the mild weather. They tell themselves a story in their mind how when it's mild outside, it's buying weather. They recognize that it's up to me to create the urgency for people to act. They focus on what they have control over, which is their attitude and actions. They talk to the client about why right now, when it's mild, is the best time to get this taken care of. They explain that the hot weather is right around the corner and when that comes, we will sometimes be backlogged for weeks, so again now is the time to act."

"Okay, so what you're saying to me is it's the exact same situation, and the person who sees it from the abundancy mentality is so much more open to the opportunities in front of them. With that perspective, I can see how almost anything is possible."

"You're right, Emily, this mindset is a gamechanger; understand it and success will come your way. So let that banner on the wall serve as a positive reminder to focus on the things we can control."

"So, Washington, why did you decide to be an installation technician?" Emily asked.

"Actually, I wasn't sure this would be my lifetime career. I started here at Champion when I was just 19. I guess you could say I was a lot like you. It didn't take long, though, for me to take pride in my job. I learned a lot about air systems and ventilation, and I learned even more about having the right values and the right mindset. It's been a great environment to be in, and I can honestly say that I love coming to work each and every day. There's always something new to learn and new people to meet and interact with. I feel like I have the best job in the world."

"You've got a great attitude, Washington! And I'm so glad I asked about the banner. It might help me deal with the disapproval I'm getting from some people," Emily admitted.

"Oh? I don't mean to pry, but is there a problem?" Washington asked with concern.

"Not really. Well, I don't know. You see, I'm a girl, and ever since I announced that I was going to be a Service Technician, I've been getting a lot of push back from some of my friends and relatives. They want me to do something more traditional with my life."

"Like what?" asked Washington.

"Like going to college to be a teacher or a nurse or…"

"Ah, yes. Well, Emily, if I can offer you a piece of advice, I'd say you need to do what's best for *you*—but remember, just like we cannot control the weather and let it influence our success, you cannot control what other people think or want and let them influence your success. Besides, it's not always what you do, but how you do it that will have the greatest impact," he offered. "Here at Champion, we have a long-term outlook, and many of the people in our company have had their lives changed by the fact that they can have a high-paying career without a four year."

"I love that, Washington, and that's something I'm going to think about and even share the next time someone questions me about the career choice I've made," said Emily.

3

GIVE REMARKABLE SERVICE

Every interaction will leave a mark.
Make it positive and memorable, so much so
that the client will remark to their friends and family.
Wow the client with your actions and a solutions-based approach.

 A few days later, Emily jumped into a company truck with Bob, a Service Technician who had been with Champion for more than 20 years. If anyone understood the company and its principles, it was Bob. He had learned them and lived them for over 2 decades, and they had been ingrained into everything he did.

Reaching for the shoulder strap of her seatbelt, Emily's eyes caught a glimpse of something taped to the dashboard. It was a smaller version of the same bright blue and red print that she had seen in the lobby around the Champion office. This time, she studied the card a bit more, noticing the headline, "Core Values."

"Hey, Bob, I've seen these all over the place, can you tell me a little more about them?" Emily asked curiously.

Bob smiled. "I like that you asked. And to answer your question, Emily, those are the core values that we all live and work by. I posted them on the dashboard because they are a powerful reminder for me, both personally and professionally."

"Wait, are they your core values or Champion's?"

"That's a good question. They are Champion's core values, and I think it's safe to say that over the years, they've become mine, too. As I've applied them at work with my clients and coworkers, I've found that they also help me in my personal life. I'm able to use them with my family and teach them to my children. I have to tell you, they've had a huge impact on my relationships with my clients and coworkers, and I've seen firsthand just how transformational they've been with my family."

"That's really neat. I've never really seen core values before I joined Champion."

"Emily, as part of your training, I'll be covering the first one specifically, which is Give Remarkable Service."

"Okay, great."

"Before we begin, let me point something out. There are six core values, and if you notice, every one of them starts with a verb, or action word. For instance, the first word in the heading is *Give*. These values are intended to be actions and behaviors and the way we operate at Champion today, versus a goal that's out there in the future.

"Now, let's dive into the first one: Give Remarkable Service. The description underneath the value reads, 'Every interaction will leave a mark. Make it positive and memorable, so much so that the client will remark to their friends and family. Wow the client with your actions and a solutions-based approach.' In order to fully understand this value, it starts with the definition of service. Do you know what the word service means?"

"Doing things for others?" she replied, taking a wild guess.

"Yes, and it's so much more than that. The definition of service is: 'Taking action to create value for someone else.' So it's more than doing something for another person—it's doing something that creates value for them—and that's important."

"Taking action ..." she repeated.

"Yes, it's more than lip service. It's about *really* taking action. This is one of the reasons each of the values starts with a verb. Are you following me?"

"Yes, I am. So when we are on our service call, the action you're going to take is to fix the client's air conditioner, and they're going to benefit from the action you took. Do I have it right?" she asked with excitement.

"You're on the right path. What we've found, Emily, is that clients *expect* us to fix their air conditioner. If our core value is to give *remarkable* service and we give our clients what they expect, do you think that's *remarkable*?" he asked, emphasizing the word.

"I suppose not."

"And do you think the client will be so wowed that they will remark to their friends and family solely because we repaired their air conditioner?" he asked.

"My guess is we'd have to do something more—kind of like going above and beyond. Am I on the right track, Bob?"

"You sure are. Before we dive into going above and beyond for the client, let me ask a few things to help you better understand. Emily, have you ever been on a boat and seen the wake that is left behind as it drives by?"

"Oh yeah, my family loves to go boating during the summer."

"Okay, great. We, too, leave a wake behind after every interaction, every day. I have the opportunity to leave a positive or negative wake in the minds and hearts of the people I visit. With the actions and words I choose to use, I have a profound impact, and that is an incredible gift we have if it is used in the right way."

"That's something to think about, and I can relate—I have always wanted people to like me."

"Yes, I can tell that about you. Let me share a positive wake story that showed up in my life at a young age. When I was in third grade, I was out on the playground playing kickball with my friends. It was time to pick teams, and kids were lining up against the wall to be chosen one at a time. Two people are selected as captains and then the choosing begins. A young classmate of mine named Damon, voiced his opinion out loud saying, 'Bob is a leader, let's have him be one of the captains.' Up to that point in my life, I had never looked at myself as a leader, or had the confidence to be such. When Damon spoke those words to me and the rest of the group, it was so profound. My chest inflated up, I set my shoulders back, and had a big smile on my face. At that moment, almost 40 years ago, I was anointed a leader. From that day forward, I've always looked at myself and carried myself as a leader in whatever I did. I've taken leadership roles at church, in my kids' school functions, and here at Champion, I've been in a team leader position for years. Damon's words have had an incredible impact on my life, and others have benefited."

"So what it sounds like you're saying, Bob, is always being aware of the impact my words and actions can have on others, both positive and negative."

"Yes, exactly, Emily. Every day, you get to decide what kind of wake you want to leave behind."

Just then, Bob pulled up to the curb and arrived at his client's home.

"Emily, I want you to watch how this first core value shows up, and then we'll discuss it in the truck together after we're finished. Okay?"

"Okay," the young girl laughed. "Hey, if you wow them enough, you might just have me remarking to *my* friends and family about it."

"Even better," Bob grinned.

Bob reached for his clipboard and skimmed over it before handing it to Emily.

"Take a look at this and see if anything stands out to you," he said, waiting until she was done.

"Um, it says here that the house is about 50 years old, and Champion installed a new air conditioning unit a little more than 10 years ago," Emily said, feeling proud of herself.

"That's right. And there's more," Bob pointed out.

"Like what?"

"You'll see," he replied, before grabbing something behind the driver's seat and putting it in his pocket.

Bob knocked on the front door, and as he waited for the homeowner to answer, Emily noticed that he looked around, taking in the carriage lights on both sides of the door, the welcome mat on the porch, and the flowerpot that hung in front of the picture window. His attention was diverted by the sound of a dog barking on the opposite side of the door.

"Be calm," he told Emily. "We want to keep the pup calm."

"Oh, hello," an older woman smiled as she opened the door. "Let me get the dog out of the way and you can come in."

"He's fine, Mrs. Thompson. I love dogs," Bob said, as the woman welcomed them in. "His name is Max, right?"

The woman responded with a smile on her face. "Yes."

Kneeling down, Bob gave Max an opportunity to get used to their presence. The dog slowly approached them, took a couple sniffs, and started to wag his tail.

"That's a good boy," Bob said, reaching out to pet his new friend. "Is it okay if I give him a treat?" he asked his client.

"Just one," she replied. "He's spoiled enough!"

Pulling a doggie snack out of his pocket, Bob reached out his hand to offer it to the dog. While the dog seemed happy to snatch it up right away, Emily noticed that it was the homeowner's face that lit up with a smile.

"Mrs. Thompson, this is Emily. She's new at Champion, and she'll be assisting me today."

"Oh, okay, great," the older woman said. "Just please excuse the mess. It takes me a bit longer to clean up nowadays."

"Oh, it's all good, just act like we're not even here—we'll do our best to stay out of your way."

Bob told Emily that the homeowner had requested service, complaining that her system was blowing warm air. Bob went down the checklist, explaining to Emily everything he was doing. When he discovered the problem, he pointed it out to her right away.

"Look, the cooling coils are dirty. We need to get these cleaned up, and we'll need to check the filter, too. It probably needs to be replaced."

As Emily began cleaning the coils, Bob walked down the hall to talk to their client. After explaining to her the problem, he went out to the truck and got a new filter. On his way back through the house, he asked if it was okay if he took a walk through the house to make sure there was adequate air throughout.

"Hey, Emily, come here for a second, will you?" he asked.

Standing in the hallway, he pointed at the vents in the two bedrooms and the bathroom, which were covered in dust and in need of a good cleaning.

"When you're done, Emily, run out to the truck and grab a couple towels from the back. We'll give these vents a good cleaning, and we'll get them dried and back on in no time."

After cleaning the vents in the living room and kitchen, they were done—except for one thing.

"Mrs. Thompson, before we go, I'm going to take a look at the air conditioner in your back yard," Bob said. "I'll be happy to let Max out while I'm back there."

"Oh, yes, thank you so much."

Once out the door, Emily watched as Max ran around the yard, obviously enjoying the outdoors. It was when Bob reached into his pocket that the dog really sprang to life. As soon as he saw the tennis ball in Bob's hand, Max started jumping and running circles around him.

"There you go, boy!" Bob said as he threw the ball to the opposite corner of the yard.

Then, turning to Emily, he asked her to grab the hose—the air conditioner was covered in months of dust and dirt.

"Simple maintenance, Emily. Keeping her system clean will improve its efficiency and make it last longer," he remarked.

Once back inside, Bob handed the tennis ball to their client.

"Here you go. I think Max really likes it. I don't have the heart to take it away from him now," he smiled.

"Oh thank you so much! You even cleaned my vents and registers. It was on my list for the next time my son comes to visit ..." her voice trailed off.

"Happy to do it, ma'am. Oh, and while I had the hose running, I gave your flowers a drink of water and washed your porch off. Before we leave, is there anything else you need?" he asked with a smile.

"You what?" the woman asked.

"Oh, I watered the flowers around the deck and then took a couple minutes to hose off the rest of the redwood area."

"You all are amazing," she smiled, shaking her head in disbelief.

"It's my pleasure, actually. Here's my card. I think you'll find that everything's running much better. I will ask our staff to give you a call tomorrow to follow up," Bob said before they departed.

Back in the truck, Bob looked at Emily and posed a question, "Do you think we gave remarkable service, according to the definition written there?"

"Boy, did you! You fixed her a/c problem, cleaned all of the register covers and vents, and the condenser! Then you watered her flowers and hosed off her deck! Wow!"

"I'm glad you noticed. Those things take very little time, and they mean a lot, especially to an elderly woman who lives alone. There was something else …"

Before he could finish, Emily exclaimed, "The dog! Max! You brought him a treat and gave him a ball! And," she gasped, "you even remembered his name! Did you notice how impressed Mrs. Thompson was when you said his name?"

Smiling, Bob pointed out to his trainee that the customer service staff had given him everything he needed to know to give remarkable service that would be of value to this homeowner. He knew she was a widow and lived alone, and he knew her birthday month. He also knew that she had a dog and that dog's name was Max.

"She's probably going to tell her daughter and everyone she knows how wonderful you were to her dog *and* how you went out of your way to do those extra things for her," Emily said.

"The amazing part is she'll remember the extra things I did more than she will that I fixed her a/c. You see, Emily, she expects us to fix her a/c. What makes it remarkable is when we do the unexpected, going beyond the HVAC. Any company can install, diagnose, and repair HVAC systems. It's our actions and attitudes that set us apart, as well as the freedom we have as team members to get creative in making the experience remarkable."

"Emily, do you remember earlier when I gave you the definition of service?"

As Emily looked down in her notepad, she said, "Yes, taking action to create value for someone else."

"Great, I'm glad you are paying attention. When you give remarkable service to a client and it makes them feel good and special, who else do you think feels good?"

"I do, the person who gave the incredible service."

"You're exactly right. We actually call that uplifting service. When you give great service, it uplifts both the client's spirits and the team member who gave the service."

"Wow, Bob, I think I'm as impressed as Mrs. Thompson must be! I also think that I'm really going to like working here," she smiled.

* * * *

At the end of the day, Emily walked through the doors that led to the support center. Joe had been on the road for two days visiting some of Champion's other service centers. Before he left, he'd invited her to stop in when he returned.

"How has your week been?" he asked.

"Unbelievable" she replied, before launching into a summary of the service call with Bob earlier that day. "You should've seen Bob—it was magic! He really impressed me, and I *know* he impressed Mrs. Thompson!"

"Yes, Bob lives and works by our values. That's one reason I made sure you partnered with him this week."

"Did you know he even has your core values posted on his dashboard? He told me that you are the one who created those values," she remarked.

"Well, I was definitely a part of creating them. It was actually the original team members who started out with me that helped create them. One day, as we were just getting off the ground, I brought the team together and asked them a question – when they write the book about Champion Air Conditioning, what do we want to be remembered for? Well, the ideas started flying as I scrambled to write everyone's thoughts and feelings on the whiteboard. Out of it all came the six defining values that guide our company and all of our decisions and actions."

"That's so cool how you got all the team involved. No wonder people seem so bought in to the core values," Emily stated. "I also saw Bob make Mrs. Thompson's day in so many ways. Whether it was with Max, her dog, or doing extra things for her around the house, he really made a difference in her day."

"I agree. You see, Emily, what we do is so much more than heating and air conditioning. We have the opportunity to change lives, one deed, one gesture, one word at a time," Joe explained.

"That's remarkable, Joe. Truly, it is," Emily replied.

"Which is precisely the reason Champion doesn't provide service—anyone can do that. We provide *remarkable* service, and that's what I want you to take away from your day. You thought you were embarking on a career as a service technician. I want you to know you have the potential to be so much more—this is your opportunity to be remarkable, Emily. It's your opportunity to provide service that uplifts our clients and *also* uplifts you. One of the reasons Bob was able to deliver remarkable service today was because our call center set him up for success and provided him with the details that they learned about the client over the phone. Whether it's knowing they have a pet or the month of their birthday, our call center goes above and beyond to help our team members deliver remarkable service. I'd really like you to spend some time with them, Emily. I'll make arrangements for you to work with Darlene—she's one of our top performers."

"Okay, great. I'm excited about that. I'll look forward to meeting her."

4

DRIVE TOP PERFORMANCE

We expect excellence from ourselves,
just as our clients expect it from us.
We measure results and reward those who deliver.
The ultimate goal is a lasting relationship.

 The next week, Emily enjoyed a cup of coffee with her fellow technicians before experiencing a new environment at Champion. Today, she was scheduled to spend time with Darlene in the call center, and she found she was excited about the change in her daily schedule and work environment, especially because Joe, whom she had come to admire, had highly recommended the experience.

"We are a meritocracy, Emily," Joe had explained. "That means your compensation is in direct proportion to your contribution. That shows up with Darlene in our call center. Number one, she wants to set the technicians up for success by giving them the data she finds by spending time with clients on the phone and developing relationships with them. She drives top performance and creates business by making outbound calls when the inbound calls aren't coming in. She's always thinking of ways to contribute."

"Hi, Darlene," Emily smiled. "Joe spoke very highly of you. I'm ready to learn what you do!"

"Wonderful. I like an enthusiastic student. Before we get started, though, is there anything you want to know? Do you have any questions?"

"Well, the first thing that caught my eye when I walked in was that poster," she said, pointing to the wall and a larger version of the core values that was taped to Bob's dashboard. "Does everyone have those core values posted in their work area?"

"You'll see reminders of our core values everywhere, Emily. You'll find them on the walls, and some of the team members have a PowerPoint of them that they use for screensavers on their computers. Some people like me even display them at home. I have a magnet with those core values on my refrigerator. They really are applicable in other areas of my life."

"That's what Bob said when I rode along with him. That day, he taught me about delivering remarkable service."

"That's something Bob does well, I assure you," Darlene added. "So since Bob already covered that, how about we focus on the second core value today, 'Drive Top Performance.'"

"How is that different from giving remarkable service? It seems to me that the two go hand in hand," asked Emily.

"The core values *are* equally important, though they are quite different. As the poster says, driving top performance is about expecting excellence from ourselves, just as our clients expect excellence from us. There's more, though. It's about measuring performance and rewarding those who deliver. Let's stop right there for a minute. Are you following me, Emily?"

"Yeah, reward those who deliver? That's the meritocracy thing Joe taught me earlier."

"Yes, it is liberating to work in a company that's a meritocracy; it's so different than other companies I've worked for."

"Emily, are you a basketball fan?"

"Yes, I'll watch the playoffs and the finals when they're on."

"There was a great player a few years back—his name was Karl Malone. Well, Karl's nickname was The Mailman, and the reason he was given that name was because his teammates could always count on him to deliver, especially when they needed him the most. I look at what I do here in the call center the same way. My teammates are counting on me to *deliver*, whether that's building a great relationship over the phone with the client in order to set our technicians up for success, or when the phones are slow, I call outbound to generate business to keep our technicians working. We take great pride in serving our clients and making sure our technicians stay busy with work so they can provide for their families. It's great teamwork that makes the dream work!"

"I love that," Emily said. "So it sounds like you enjoy doing what you do?"

"Do I? I *love* what I do, mostly because I know that I'm contributing to our clients and to our company. It's incredibly rewarding.

"What I love about Champion is that when I drive top performance and generate business, I am contributing more. Therefore, I'm compensated more. It's a great opportunity to make more money. In that way, my income is limitless—I can impact how much I make every day," Darlene said. "It motivates me to deliver the best service I can to our clients and our company."

"Joe explained a little about that to me. I'd like to learn how you do it," Emily replied.

"It's all about results, Emily. Our results are tracked, and we get reports every day that show how we perform amongst our peers."

"Everybody gets to see that? Does that ever make you feel uncomfortable, especially if others are performing better?" Emily asked with a questioning look on her face.

"Yes, everyone sees the reports, and that's okay. I've learned to embrace it. When we're enjoying success, we are so open to sharing. I've worked for other companies that were the polar opposite. There were times when the top performers were reluctant to share their secrets, almost like they were afraid someone would steal their spot. Here at Champion, we have a different environment. Everyone wants to share because they *want* their peers to succeed. It's just part of our culture. Many of us at Champion have been through leadership training that emphasizes that givers gain, takers lose. So, at every turn our first instinct is to give and share, rather than take. It's liberating to work for a company that encourages, and I'd say, even demands that," said Darlene.

"So it's not a competition?"

"There's definitely a friendly competition, balanced with a giving heart. I like to explain it this way: you get what you give. So, share your successes and what's working for you, and more success will come your way.

"That's why we are so transparent. Here, let me show you," she said, pulling up the daily report on the computer and explaining what it revealed.

"I understand," Emily offered. "These sales reports show the top performers, and they motivate you to do your best!"

"Yes, these reports also allow me to know where I stand against my goal daily. All the great performers at Champion 'know thy numbers.' What I mean by that is, they take full responsibility and accountability to the performance numbers. They treat it like it's their own business and have a tremendous amount of passion for achieving the desired result. Know that the sales performance report is just one part of driving top performance. The other part is client satisfaction scores."

"How do you know those scores?"

"Again, it's daily transparency. That's right, Emily, we receive a client satisfaction report every day, as well. Having high sales must be balanced with client satisfaction. You must have both!"

Darlene opened another report, showing the young technician the morning's client satisfaction report. When Emily asked where the scores come from, she explained that it was part of their follow-up activities.

"After every appointment, our clients are sent a survey that asks three questions. Clients score us on a scale of one to ten."

"And the goal is to get a 10 ... am I right?"

"Close. Actually, our minimum expectation is 9.75, and our reports show that we're tracking above that," Darlene answered.

"What happens if clients don't score you well?"

"In that case, we contact them to determine why they weren't fully satisfied. Once we know that, we set out to make it right and earn that top score. That might mean going back and addressing the issue or refunding their money."

"Wow. That's not something you see every day," Emily remarked.

"That's true, and that's something that sets apart a company that focuses on top performance. It also places a focus on accountability," the trainer said.

"Does that cause you to feel a lot of pressure?" Emily asked.

"Top performers love to be held accountable. It drives them; it's what makes them strive to be even better. Non-performers shy away from accountability. Here at Champion, either a non-performer becomes a performer, or they move on to another company. Emily, I'm a huge baseball fan, and business is so much like baseball when it comes to tracking data. The general manager of the Oakland A's said it well. 'Welcome to the Oakland A's, where the pleasure in performing exceeds the pressure to perform.'"

"Oh, I like that!" Emily's response was enthusiastic.

Darlene smiled. "That saying holds true in every department at Champion. Whether you're a third baseman in professional baseball or you're a representative in our call center, the pleasure in a job well done outweighs the pressure to make it happen."

"I'd like to see it in action, Darlene," Emily commented.

"Sure thing. Let's get on the phone and make a few calls to give you a better idea of how it's done."

Emily listened intently as Darlene communicated with clients. It struck her that Darlene was exceptionally good at what she did. From the onset, she was both professional and friendly. It was almost like she had a knack for making the person on the phone feel at ease, so much that they freely offered information and details about themselves and their needs. As Emily listened, she began to see how even the smallest detail could have an impact on delivering remarkable service, which in turn, would naturally influence their ability to drive top performance.

When they were done, Emily shared her new insight.

"You're really good at what you do, Darlene," she remarked. "I imagined being the client during your calls, and to me, they all seemed to be delighted with the way you took care of them."

"Thank you. It's all a part of the Driving Top Performance core value. What's most important is the last sentence, where it states:

'Our ultimate goal is a lasting relationship.' You see, Emily, I can drive top performance, make sales, make a lot of money for me and my family. What I always remember and live by is that last sentence, which is creating a lasting relationship.

"I can clearly see how you do that. And I can see how big of a role you play here in the call center in doing that," said Emily.

"I'm glad to hear it. How about we make one more call before we take a break? I need to call the Spencer family and set up a maintenance appointment."

Darlene introduced herself to the homeowner and told her the purpose of the call.

"I'm just calling to schedule your next tune up and service," she informed the client.

"I didn't realize we're due already, but I guess it has been a while. The last time you were here was the end of the year, and now I'm tending to my garden already," Mrs. Spencer said.

"Oh, you have a green thumb? What do you grow?" Darlene asked.

"Roses, I just love them. They do take some time, but they're worth it. Besides, I really do enjoy it."

"I can imagine that they're beautiful," Darlene commented.

"They are, but I'm particularly excited this year. Last fall, I added a hybrid that just started budding and should be blooming any day now. It should be a spectacular mix of vibrant coral and pink colors. It promises to be a showstopper when it blooms. I simply cannot wait to see it!" the client explained.

"Oh, that does sound unique. I'd love to see it, too! As a matter of fact, one of these days, I'm going to make sure I do!" replied Darlene.

"You're welcome anytime. There's nothing I enjoy more than showing off my roses. They're my pride and joy," said Mrs. Spencer.

After speaking for a few more minutes, Darlene told the client that Brandon would arrive at 9 a.m. the next Tuesday. "I'll keep my fingers crossed for sunshine every day, so your new rose bush will be in full bloom by then!"

As Darlene was completing the call, she entered notes about the equipment, arrival time, etc. What took Emily by surprise was all the notes entered about the client's love of gardening and the specific colors of the roses that will be blooming any day.

"Why the notes about her gardening and roses?" Emily asked.

"Well, anything I can do to help the technician build a relationship and find common ground."

Emily remembered back to when she rode with Bob and how the dog's name, Max, was there in the notes.

"Wow! I saw that when Bob called the dog by name, the client was blown away!"

"We call that Emotional Resonance. We are looking to help build a deep emotional connection between the client and our company," explained Darlene.

"That's cool! What company nowadays takes the time to do that?" Emily asked.

"We do! And I'm proud to be a part of it," Darlene said with a smile.

Once Darlene completed her notes, she grabbed a form from a tray on her desk.

"What's that? A service ticket?" Emily asked.

"No. Everything we do is automated. In that way, our technicians and salespeople can access all of the information on file for every client. This form is a request to accompany Brandon on the appointment," she explained.

"Who? You?" Emily asked, sounding confused.

"Yes. I think I'd like to take Mrs. Spencer up on her offer and see her roses in all their glory."

"Really, Darlene? That would make her day!" Emily exclaimed.

"I think it'll make my day, too, Emily," Darlene smiled.

5

HONOR YOUR COMMITMENTS

We follow through with what we say we're going to do;
this behavior is critical in building trust.

 Over the course of the next couple weeks, Emily became more familiar with the people she worked with, including a couple people who were quickly becoming friends. They sought each other out during the work week and got together outside of work on a few occasions. In school, being popular hadn't been important to her. Sure, she had friends, most of which were fellow members of her cheer squad, which wasn't surprising since they spent so much time together. Now that they had graduated and moved on, though, their texts and interactions had lessened. Emily knew this was natural. People moved on, making new friendships while pursuing new interests. That was why she was surprised when she received a text from one of the former members of her cheer squad, asking for a ride to the school the following week.

"Hey, can you maybe pick me up on your way to summer camp on Friday?"

It took a minute before Emily realized what she was referring to, and then it dawned on her. Every summer, the cheer squad from the previous year held a camp for the students who wanted to try out for a place on the squad. They taught them cheers and helped them perfect their skills, preparing them for tryouts, as well as the various competitions they'd enter during the year. Even though they had graduated, they were expected to participate in the camp, and Emily had been aware of it. As a matter of fact, her coaches had given them a packet with the details on the last day of school.

However, time changes things. Emily now had a job, and she was reluctant to ask for time off, especially for summer camp. Surely, she thought, there would be exceptions to the requirement. Besides, what could they do to her if she sat the camp out? She'd already received her diploma, after all. The more she thought about it, the more she convinced herself that she wasn't needed. Her job was more important. Surely, her coach and squad members would understand.

"Hi, Brooke!" she replied. "I'd like to help you out if I could, but I won't be able to be there Friday. I have to work. Good luck!"

Emily knew she had to let the coach know that she couldn't make it, and she told herself she would. For some reason, though, it was a conversation she preferred to delay.

* * * *

At Champion, Emily had gotten used to the routine. She knew precisely what to do when she arrived in the morning and what to expect throughout the day. Her favorite times, though, were when she got to meet with Joe. Thus far, they had been meeting once a week on average, with the exception of the previous week, when Joe had been at their academy conducting training for their team members. After not seeing him for two weeks, Emily was looking forward to their meeting that Monday afternoon.

When he asked her how she liked working with Darlene in the call center, she told him what a positive experience it was.

"It was really cool to see how committed she is to our clients, Joe. They're always friendly, and I walked away with the impression that Darlene really likes her job—and the clients. What really impressed me, though, was when Darlene put in a request to go on a service call because she told one of the clients that she would love to see her roses. Then she promised her that one day she would! I followed up with her the next week, and she actually did! To hear her say it, Mrs. Spencer was very pleasantly surprised and more than happy to show off her green thumb!"

"I'm glad to hear it. Darlene has always been an exceptional representative of our team. She is quite knowledgeable, and clients state that she's extremely helpful and, yes, friendly. She's definitely an asset to us here at Champion, which is one reason why I wanted you to spend some time with her. And the fact that she personally visited a client is par for the course with Darlene. If she says she's going to do something, we can all count on the fact that she will. It's one of her many admirable contributions to the call center and, frankly, to our entire organization," said Joe.

Suddenly, Emily remembered the cheer camp, and she felt a wave of guilt. She tried to justify her decision in an attempt to dismiss it.

"I get it, Joe. I'm really beginning to feel like I belong here and like I'm committed to making you and everyone else know that you can count on me. That's why I decided not to participate in my high school's summer camp this Friday. I have graduated, after all, and when I agreed to do it, I didn't have this job. Of course, my job is my priority. The cheer squad and my coach will just have to understand that," Emily explained.

Joe was silent for a moment as he digested what Emily had said. When he spoke, his response was not what she expected.

"Emily, I know you've seen our core values, and I think there is one that I'd like to talk to you about today, if you have time," he said.

"Sure, Joe," Emily smiled as she looked at the core values framed on the wall. "Which one?"

"Honor your commitments," Joe answered. "When I think of this core value, I think of two things, Emily. First, I think of Ray, our Vice President of Operations, who says that if we fail to follow through on our promises, we need to address it in a certain way. Ray puts it quite eloquently: we always want our client to feel like we are running toward them, rather than away from them."

"I think that's a wonderful perspective. I'll have to remember that," she replied.

"Mistakes may happen, and while we do our best to minimize

them, we also have to correct them when they happen. Sometimes we might experience a scheduling error, or perhaps there will be times when the equipment we need isn't available. Things happen. When they do, though, we have to remember that running away from those situations only serves to compound the issue. That's why we run toward them, doing what we have to do to make it right as quickly as we can."

"How do you do that?"

"For one thing, we have an on-time guarantee. So if we do have a scheduling error and aren't on time, the service call is free. When we are at fault, we admit it and correct it. It's one way that we honor our commitments."

"Emily, the core value is to follow through with what we say we are going to do. This behavior is critical to building trust. When someone asks me to do something and I agree to do it, I follow through. It goes a long way in establishing and maintaining trust. On top of that, I find that I really enjoy following through on my promises."

"But, Joe, what if you can't? I mean, what if you make a promise, but your circumstances change, and you have new commitments that are more important?"

"Ahh, that's a good question. My best advice is to be careful when making commitments. When you make too many, you will chip away at your self-esteem because you will not be able to honor them, which will cause you to lose confidence in yourself. I make every attempt to only make commitments that I fully intend to honor. I recommend that you limit the number of commitments you make, and when you do make commitments, write them down so you will be sure to follow through. That's what I do, and even more, I review my journal regularly to make sure I remember each and every one of them. That serves two purposes. First, when I write a commitment down, it solidifies it, making it like a written contract. And then my journal is like a calendar or to-do list, if you will, that serves as a reminder that I have an obligation, whether it is to others or to myself. "

"But what if a commitment was an obligation, but one that you intended to carry out at the time, but a more important commitment came up later?" she asked.

"What's going on, Emily?" Joe asked. "Is there something you want to share with me?"

Slightly embarrassed, Emily launched into her situation, telling Joe about the requirement to be a coach at the high school summer camp.

"But, Joe, that was before I had this job. Naturally, that's an exception. Right?"

"The fact that circumstances changed later is a challenge that will happen in your life. I want you to seriously consider how it affects other people when you fail to honor your commitments. Let me ask you a question: what would happen if everyone on the cheer squad felt the same way and decided it wasn't important to show up at the summer camp? Put yourself in others' shoes—were you the recipient of the time and effort of summer camp coaches? Was that important to you at the time?"

"I guess so," Emily answered sheepishly.

"I think you know the answer. I think it was important to you, which is why you're torn right now. Am I right?" Joe smiled knowingly.

"Yes, but there's nothing I can do about it. I mean, I can't let you down or the team that's counting on me here," Emily justified.

"Like I said, things happen. I understand that, and so does our entire team. It's my firm belief that honoring our commitments, even when we don't absolutely have to or don't want to, is most important. I admire someone who does that because it's the foundation of what we stand for. You made a commitment, Emily."

"I did," Emily sighed. "And you're right. I think one reason it was nagging at me was because I felt guilty about backing out on my team. I guess I was looking for you to tell me it was okay in this instance if I didn't go. Thank you for helping me see it in the right light. So, Joe, I guess I just have one more question."

"What's that?"

"Do I have permission to take Friday off?" she smiled.

"Sure. Now that we've settled that, let's take a minute to talk about how honoring our commitments impacts us at Champion and our clients. Let me give you an example. We sold a system to a client, who expressed concern that she wouldn't be able to be home during the installation. Our Manager, Lyndy, indicated to the client that she understood and came up with a solution by volunteering to be there in the client's home during the install. And on the day of the install, Lyndy followed through. She made a temporary workstation at the client's kitchen table, where she worked all day, checking in on the progress of the installation, while also communicating with the client about the progress. In the end, the client's concerns were addressed, and we established trust with her. She knew we weren't making empty promises. And it's all because we followed through and honored our commitments," Joe said.

"That's impressive. You know, Joe, the stories I keep hearing about how our team members go the extra mile amaze me!"

"I'm quite proud of the team and the fact that they take our core values seriously, Emily. I was just talking about this with Shannon, one of our top salespeople, the other day. She lives and breathes by this core value, and I think she can add to this conversation. Let me see if I can get her on the line," he said, reaching for the phone.

"Hi, Shannon," Joe said. "I am talking to one of our young and promising technicians, and we started discussing the importance of honoring our commitments. I immediately thought of you and your remarks about this core value last week. Do you mind if I put you on speakerphone so you can share your insight with Emily?"

"I'd be happy to, Joe!" Shannon readily agreed. "Emily, welcome to the Champion team! I feel honored that Joe chose me to share this core value with you because it's one of my personal favorites. I've seen firsthand just how much impact it has on our relationships with our clients. It's super important to follow through with what you state you're going to do because this behavior builds trust, which is vital to my success and the success of our company."

"When I make a sales presentation to a client, I always let them know about our company. They really do need to know more than what product they're buying—they need to know who they're giving their trust and hard-earned money to. When I tell them about me and our company, I share our core values. There's even a page in my binder that lists them. Every time I go over that page, I specifically talk about two of our core values. One is 'give remarkable service,' the other is 'honoring our commitments.' Like I said, they're my two favorites."

"How do you honor your commitments in your role, Shannon?" Emily asked.

"There are multiple ways to do that, and multiple things I do to make sure I follow through with it. When I'm at a client's home and they're buying a new system, there are specific things that might have to be altered, such as relocating the equipment. So I tell the client upfront just what we are going to do and what the project entails. In addition to writing those details down when completing the paperwork, I make a video recording of what we're going to do for the install team. The video shows the installers the details they need to know, such as the layout of the house, which helps us follow through with what we say we're going to do. Their job is then easier because they know what they need to do and how they're going to do it ahead of time."

"That must make it easier for them to prepare," Emily commented.

"It sure does. And it reinforces our ability to do what we tell the client we are going to do. I take it one step further—when I leave the client's home or as it gets closer to the actual installation, I call the Install Manager to share the details. This helps that team member select the best crew for that specific project."

"That's a great idea!"

"I know it helps. It might seem like a small task, but it can make a big difference! The details are really helpful. With those details and the video, I'm able to show the team more than the layout. For instance, they can see that the client has immaculate white carpet, so before they even get to the door, they know they have to be extra diligent and careful. Or they might notice that the family has a dog, and I'll mention it, as well, even sharing the dog's name with our team."

"So, it's like all the members of the team know the project and the client before they even meet them," Emily said.

"Yes, absolutely. I want to make sure they know what I've learned during the sales process. I do want you to know, though, that my job doesn't stop once I have the sale. I like to think of myself as more than a salesperson. For example, after the sale and the planning are completed, it's common for me to stop by on the day of the install to make sure everything is going well and the client is happy. It's important to me to make sure we are honoring the commitments I made to the homeowner."

"Yes, Joe just told me about a manager who stayed at the house during the installation because the client couldn't be there! I thought that was incredible," Emily commented.

"I believe our clients deserve that level of service and following through with all of our promises and assurances is part of that. Buying a new HVAC system is a large investment. It's not like buying a toaster. Our clients need to have confidence that we do stand by our product, our service, and our word. It's a level of commitment that is lacking among businesses, and I love seeing how impressed our clients are when they see that we follow through on every promise we make," Shannon said.

"It's giving remarkable service!" Emily added.

"Yes, and that's why those are my two favorite core values. They go hand in hand. There's more, though. When you consider all of Champion's core values, you can begin to see how they can each stand on their own. However, the one core value that all of the others depend on is to honor our commitments. We are committed to giving remarkable service, and to make sure it happens, we have to honor that commitment. Do you get what I'm saying?" Shannon asked.

"I sure do! In order for any of the core values to be truly effective, we have to be committed to them. Am I right?"

"Yes, you are. You're a fast learner, Emily," Shannon said. "Please ask Joe to share my contact information with you. If you have any questions or if there is anything I can do for you, feel free to let me know!"

"I really like her, Joe," Emily stated when the call ended. "She seems so friendly and helpful."

"She is both, Emily, and I'm glad she made a good impression on you. I called Shannon because I thought she could actually explain this core value better than I can. It's so ingrained in her that she doesn't even think about it anymore. It's part of who she is and how she conducts business."

"What would she do if she had made a commitment to coach a high school cheer squad the year before?" Emily asked, already knowing the answer.

"She would go, and she would give 100 percent to the task at hand—and it's probably safe to guess that she would follow up when she was done to make sure they were happy, and perhaps, even send them a card, thanking them for the opportunity to serve them," Joe smiled.

"Well, then, it looks like I better practice up on some of my cheers and tumbling, Joe. I'm going to honor my commitment, and I'm going to make sure I give it my all. My coach and fellow squad members deserve that, and so do the students," Emily said.

"So do you, Emily. Remember, when you honor your commitments, you boost your own confidence and self-esteem. When other people trust you, you learn to trust yourself."

6

BE A LIFELONG STUDENT

Be open to learning and new possibilities.
Continue to challenge yourself
and get outside your comfort zone.

 The next Friday, Emily picked up her friend, Brooke, for the all-day summer cheer camp.

Sighing when she climbed into the car, Brooke was still in the process of pulling her hair back into a ponytail.

"Hi, Emily. Whoa, 7:30 is too early for me. Who in their right mind starts summer camp at 8:00 a.m.? I mean, it's *summer!* I haven't gotten up this early since we graduated."

Laughing, Emily shrugged off her friend's comment.

"Really? I guess I'm used to it. I'm out the door by this time every day," she said.

"That's crazy! After all, like I said, it *is* summer. Summers are for sleeping in. Come August, I have early classes two days a week!"

Brooke moaned.

"What I've learned, Brooke, in the short time I've been at Champion is, if you are doing something you are passionate about, getting up is easy."

"I guess I've yet to find my passion," Brooke retorted.

Walking through the heavy metal double doors, a wave of familiarity hit Emily as she stepped back into the school where she'd spent the last four years of her life. It was exactly as she'd left it—nothing had changed, except the halls were empty and quiet, so quiet that it seemed like any noise at all would echo and be heard across the entire building.

"Funny, the school looks smaller," Brooke said. "But maybe that's compared to my college. The university is *huge*! I just know I'm going to get lost!"

"I'm sure you'll be fine. Remember how scared we were the first day we walked into this building?" Emily reminded her.

To Emily, it was as if time had stood still when she walked into the gym. It was almost as if she could hear the fans and see the players running across the highly polished wood floor.

And once the camp got underway, she felt right at home as she coached the students through cheers and tumbling, teaching them how to maneuver through the moves and coordinate their timing. Some students had experience, while others were new, both to high school and cheerleading. Emily found she had something to offer all of them.

At the end of the day, she took her group aside and gave them a pep talk and a few pointers.

"Always keep a smile on your face. Act confident and then you will be filled with confidence. Fake it 'til you make it. You're representing your school, inside or outside of this gym, and being on the cheer squad is a privilege and a commitment. Make sure you're prepared to honor that commitment—your squad is depending on you, and so is your school. Good luck, ladies! I hope to see you when I come back to watch a game!"

Settled back into the car, Brooke heaved an exaggerated sigh of exhaustion.

"Whew! It's been a *long* day!" she exclaimed.

"I enjoyed it more than I thought I would," Emily replied. "Actually, it was nice to go back again."

"It was okay, but I think you always liked school more than I did, Emily, which is why I'm kind of surprised that you're not going to college. Out of all of us, you were the most focused. In my opinion, you were the one 'most likely to' succeed and really make something of yourself. You have so much potential that I think it's a shame that you're not applying it to anything. Don't you want to *be somebody* someday, Emily? I mean, is working for an air conditioning company really your dream?" Brooke asked.

Taken aback by her friend's words, Emily was surprised to hear them. *Is that what people really think—that I'm not living up to my potential? That I'm not applying myself, or that because I'm not going to college, I'm not making a rewarding career for myself?*

Finally, she mustered a response.

"Brooke, maybe college isn't for everybody. I've met a lot of highly successful people who never went on to school, and I hope to be one of them one day, too. And I do think this might be my dream job. I know I like what I'm doing, so I'm going to give it some time. Who knows what'll happen? I might just surprise you. Maybe I'll even surprise myself."

* * * *

Still, Brooke's words stuck with her over the course of the weekend. When she thought about them, she also remembered that her mom had expressed similar thoughts. Or were they doubts? While both of them might have believed they had her best interests at heart, she wondered if they had any idea how much she wished she had their support and approval.

She shared some of those thoughts with Joe the next week, who listened quietly to what she said—and what she didn't say. When she was done, he could sense that she was uneasy with what her friend had said.

"Emily, do you believe you are learning here at Champion?"

"Sure! I've learned so much, although I do know that I need to learn a whole lot more," she answered.

"Good. I want you to recognize that learning can happen anywhere and anytime. It is not restricted to formal educational institutions. That said, I am and always have been a strong advocate for a good education, which again comes in many forms. And I encourage all of our team members to be open to every opportunity to increase their knowledge and skills. But there are different types of learning—some are experience-based, while others open our eyes to new possibilities and opportunities. They help us grow beyond the traditional academic classroom. I like to think of the learning we provide here as growth that helps us discover and utilize our real gifts and talents," Joe said.

"I know you've always encouraged me to grow, and you've gone out of your way to mentor me. You've really taught me a lot!" Emily said.

"What I want you to realize is that you are receiving a *real* education here at Champion—it's an integral part of what our company is about. Unlike college, though, our philosophy is that learning never ends. It's a process, and it's part of life. I understand that your family and friends might have expressed misgivings about your choice of careers, and they probably *do* mean well. It's just that your career choice is outside of their comfort zone. I encourage you to continue to challenge yourself and get outside of *your* comfort zone. At Champion, you are going to be challenged, whether it be through speaking in front of a group or role playing in front of your peers. You might even be asked to teach a class. It's all with the intent that those new experiences will help you grow so you can be the best you can be. It's the self-development component that makes our company unique."

"Like your core values?" Emily interjected.

"Exactly. I look at Champion as a people-development company, more than an air conditioning business. That's actually why I started my own company. I wanted to influence a lot of people and help develop them to be the best version of themselves," he explained. "Throughout the years, I've discovered that the only way I can make Champion better is to make the people *inside* Champion better. It's what I do with my family, too. I help my kids improve on their skills, whether they're playing baseball or working on multiplication tables. I want to help them to be their best. I bring that same passion to our team members. One team member who really comes to mind is Kyle. Years ago, he was the deli manager at the athletic club I went to. He waited on me for years, and I noticed that he was always cheerful and he always had a great attitude. He was the poster child for our hiring philosophy, which is that we hire for attitude and train for skill."

"Oh, I like that!" Emily responded.

"We know we can train and teach people how to carry out their responsibilities. It's a bit more difficult to teach someone how to adopt a great attitude. Well, Kyle had that attitude we were looking for. Anyway, it came to my attention that he won the title of Employee of the Year at the athletic club, and that really made me take notice and interest in him. As I got to know him better, I made an effort to learn more about him and ask questions. What were his goals? His dreams? He told me he was going to junior college, and I began to talk to him about our industry and something I want to bring to your attention: Champions University."

"Champions University that I read about on your website?" Emily questioned.

"Yes. You will be enrolled in the next class, Emily, so I want you to know a few things about Champions University. It is a legitimate learning institution, though our terms are much shorter than traditional colleges and universities. For example, we have an eight-week program for service technicians like yourself. It's a highly skilled and accelerated program. You might like our slogan, which is 'a high-paying career without a four year.'"

"I love that! It's catchy."

"We're in the trades, and we know that so many, like your friend Brooke, believe that every good job requires a four-year degree. At Champions University, we teach the skills necessary for a rewarding and lucrative career without the four-year investment of time and money. You'll find it's rigorous, and I'm confident that you're going to learn a great deal during that time, like Kyle and our other service technicians have. Yes, we hired Kyle, and he attended Champions University. He started as a technician and worked his way up the Career Path. Today, he's one of our Service Managers and is doing remarkably well. You have that opportunity, too. You can have a rewarding career and the specialized training you need to excel in it. At the same time, you'll be challenged to grow and be the very best you can be. It is our philosophy that sets us apart from four-year institutions, and it's what sets our people apart. I guess you can say that they learn all of the time, every day."

"Joe, I have to say it sounds interesting. I'm glad we had this talk. I'm kind of embarrassed to admit that I was doubting myself, wondering if I was doing the right thing. Now, I'm sure I am! I'm really excited about the opportunity to attend Champions University."

"And I'm excited for your class to begin. It is a very positive experience, one where team members join in the learning process. We've had salespeople teach service technicians, and vice versa. And no matter where you're at in your career, most people find that the teachers learn as much as the students. You might say that while they fill their students' cups, their cups are also filled. In fact, many of them walk out of the university and into some of their best days here at Champion. For example, some of our salespeople have their highest sales days right after returning from Champions University, and they credit their experience there with that accomplishment."

"Really? That sounds awesome. I'm sure I'll benefit from it," Emily said.

"I want you to know, Emily, that while you will be attending our university for a specific window of time, in your case, eight weeks, Champion views learning as a lifelong process. We know that there is always an opportunity to learn something new, always an opportunity to grow and improve, both in our careers and as people. I use the word 'challenge' when I talk about learning, because I want to challenge everyone to be the best they can be. Of course, that benefits everyone here in the company, mostly *you*. Learning is a gift you give to yourself, for life. It's a gift that you'll always have, and it will benefit you in everything you do."

"Joe, what you're saying sounds so much like what I've been feeling. And what's really neat is that what you're offering me is so much more than college! It's more than four years and done," Emily pointed out.

"I was hoping you'd see it that way. Now, let's sit down and go over the details so I can make sure you get into the next session."

* * * *

Four weeks later, Emily walked into Champions University and was immediately impressed. The building was immaculate and very specifically set up to teach every aspect of Champion's business. There was a university lab that held heating and air conditioning equipment, where technicians learned the parts and how to service them under the guidance and supervision of observers and instructors. And just like other schools, there were classrooms, where instructors shared their knowledge, teaching HVAC skills, as well as their company-specific values.

Joe had prepared her, telling her that Champion's culture was all about the top performers sharing their secrets and giving coaching to the new technicians. Having those top performers return to the classroom as instructors was an effective way to share their knowledge and success secrets with newcomers to the company, keeping them fresh and alive among everyone. He told her to expect to be the recipient of those "lessons" and inside tips, keeping in mind that one day, she, too, might be the one providing her insights to new members of the company.

The first morning, she was in a group where they learned how to introduce themselves to clients effectively. This involved getting on a first-name basis quickly and perfecting the ability to give clients a sincere compliment upon their first meeting.

"Make sure you're keeping the client engaged by asking great questions! If you're doing all the talking, you'll lose the client," Ed, the Champions University instructor, said. On the outside, Ed was a strong, burly man with a powerful voice to match. It was apparent to everyone who knew him, though, that he was a gentle giant. He trains the students to be great service technicians; moreover, he teaches them to be great human beings.

"Another thing to remember is to make sure you speak clearly and with confidence. Avoid the tendency to fill up silent moments with uhs, and ahs, and umms," he added. "That gives the impression that you are uncertain or lack confidence in your recommendation."

After receiving the tips, it was the technicians' turns to demonstrate what they'd learned. Through a role-playing process, they introduced themselves and went through each step. Then the observers provided their feedback, and the technician was then given another opportunity to repeat the exercise—again and again, receiving feedback to help them improve every time.

What Emily really liked was that nobody was insulted or made to feel inferior. There was no embarrassment when improvement was necessary, just sincere encouragement and positive feedback with the sole intent to improve. It was all about learning, applying, feedback, and practice, practice, practice!

Ed explained the process, pointing to a large sign on the wall.

"EDICR, it's an acronym for how we train and practice a new concept. The E stands for explanation. We explain the proper way to introduce yourself—be engaged with the client when you're introducing yourself and the 'why' behind the way we do it. The D represents demonstrate—we show the technician how to do it. Then there's I, which stands for imitate. You get to imitate exactly what you just saw, what was demonstrated. The next step is the C—correction. You might think of it as feedback, though we call them gifts—gifts for improvement, gifts to help you make more money! The first gift you'll get is positive feedback, letting you know what you did well. Then that's followed up with the gifts for improvement, which are always delivered with encouragement. Can anyone guess what the R stands for?"

"Redo?" Emily guessed.

"Very close! It's repetition," the instructor said.

"Oh, so you've got to do it all over again until you get it right?" one of the students asked.

"You *get* to do it all over again, and the fact that you *get* to do it until you've mastered it is our gift to you," Ed explained.

Her time at Champions University was a phenomenal experience. She learned so very much about servicing HVAC systems, and even more about Champion's philosophy. Emily walked away from her first week amazed at the positivity and encouragement that she received, and she truly felt that she had made the right career choice. She vowed that she would make sure that Joe felt he made the right choice in hiring her.

She couldn't stop talking about what an amazing experience it was when Joe checked in with her at the end of the week.

"I learned so much. It was incredible, and so were the people! If I can, I'd love to come back every year. Is that possible?" she asked excitedly.

"I expect that you *will* return, Emily—perhaps in another capacity, such as an observer or an instructor. As a matter of fact, we encourage it. You'll discover that you learn something new every time," Ed said. "You're learning how to be a service technician at Champion, but I think you'll discover that you're also learning how to be a leader."

"Do you really think I can be a leader someday, Joe?"

"I know you can. Embrace learning, apply it, and be open to suggestions for growth—it's what Champions University is all about," the mentor said.

* * * *

While Emily had chosen a different path than college, she was delighted to find just how much she enjoyed Champions University. Every day, she learned something new, and the next day built on the day before, taking her knowledge and skills a step farther.

And she was relieved to find that she was a quick learner, easily skating through the classes and then applying her knowledge in a simulated setting, whether within a group or in the lab. While some of the other technicians seemed to have to really work at it, she breezed through the two-month program.

Even the final test … their program concluded with two tests that required an 80 percent score or higher. In these tests, they had to stand in front of a panel consisting of three managers who graded them on a presentation—all while being observed by their classmates. Their training and education culminated with these tests, and their employment at Champion depended on successfully passing it. Of course, this caused stress and quite a bit of anxiety for the students, who spent hours and hours practicing and rehearsing to make sure they were prepared.

The one saving grace was that, like in the repetition portion of their other demonstrations, the students got two chances to pass the panel tests, and there were a handful of students who needed the second opportunity to improve their grade. However, Emily nailed it, earning an 89 percent on her first panel test and an impressive 92 percent on the second test. Her success provided her with the validation she needed to know in her heart that she could be good at her job and that it was a great career choice.

She was still celebrating when she returned to Champion and advised Joe that she had officially earned her "degree."

"I'm glad to hear that it was a great learning experience!" Joe congratulated. "Now I challenge you to continue your quest for knowledge. It's always been my belief that learning is a never-ending process, especially if you want to grow over the years. Remember on our first day together, I shared with you that leaders are readers? I challenge you to figure out a way to build a habit of continuous, lifelong learning, where you are getting in at least ten pages of reading in a day. It will benefit your growth and progress tremendously. You see, if you're reading, you're working on improving yourself. There's a quote that I like to tell the team members here at Champion, 'If you want to make a living, work hard at your job. If you want to make a fortune, work hard on yourself.'"

"Joe, that's another great saying. You really do have a way with words," she complimented.

"Thank you, Emily. I want you to know that I know you'll work hard here at Champion, and I'm certain you'll make a great living. If you really want to take your income, your health, and your relationships to the next level, which truly is the fortune, you have to work on yourself. Reading is one way. Taking regular time for yourself to rest is another. Exercising and eating right is also so important. Being disciplined in these areas, taking care of yourself, and working on yourself is really where the fortune is made."

"Oh, I will definitely try. I want to learn as much as I can," Emily said.

"Try, Emily? You'll find that here at Champion we think the word 'try' is a weak word, and we want you to eliminate it from your vocabulary. We'll help you when we hear you say it, and we'll even correct you by just repeating 'try' in a questioned response, then letting you replace it with a word like 'do' or 'will.' Those are powerful words—words that when you speak them, gives you confidence to achieve or accomplish whatever it is that you're after."

"I like that! While we're talking about eliminating weak words from my vocabulary, are there any others that come to mind that you can help me with?"

"There sure are. Some words to eliminate are 'could' or 'should,' both of which can be replaced with 'will.' For example, saying, 'I *should* read ten pages a day' becomes 'I will read ten pages a day.' Notice how much more powerful that sounds and how much more confidence you feel when you say it."

"I *will* read ten pages a day," Emily repeated with audible confidence.

"Well done, Emily," Joe smiled. "You are a great student, and I like that you immediately apply what you've learned, which sears it in your mind for future use."

"Thanks, Joe. Every time I talk with you, I learn something. You, everyone here at Champion, and Champions University have taught me so much."

"It's great that we have Champions University where you can learn, and keep in mind that the real work is just now beginning. When it comes to being a lifelong student, the real work comes *after* you graduate," Joe said.

"What do you mean?" Emily asked, confused.

"I call it 'CANI,'" he explained, spelling out the acronym. "It stands for Constant And Never-Ending Improvement. Continuous learning is the key to our success, and it will play a vital role in yours. We did our job and put you through the training; now, we're handing it over to you to live this core value from this day forward. Emily, your journey has just begun."

7

HAVE FUN AND ENJOY THE MOMENT

Be present and in the now! Life is short, life is precious.
Be happy with what is going right.
Focus on progress, measure backwards!

 Having successfully graduated from Champions University and completing her on-the-job training, Emily's confidence in her career choice and her ability to be successful grew. She loved her job and the company and was all in, fully committed to doing her best.

After doing so well at the university, she expected only sunny days ahead. It was easy for her to study, practice, and apply what she had learned about the trade, which the university coined to be the SPA Principle. She transformed into a great student of success, which included seeking out people who were successful and studying what they were doing. Emulating Joe's success path, she modeled those successful people, copying their actions and saying what they said, while still making it her own.

In high school, she had been focused and wanted to do well, in spite of the fact that she had little interest in her classes. As she learned more and more about the trade and studied other successful people in the trade, her interest and confidence flourished, and so did her results. Emily tripled her income in her first year at Champion and realized that the more valuable she became in the marketplace, the more income she made. And she discovered just how to become more valuable—by implementing the SPA Principle.

Everything was going well. While her former high school classmates were back in the classroom for another four years, Emily had already begun to put her education to use and had a respectable job with benefits. A high-paying career without a four-year—she felt like she'd hit the jackpot.

She walked into her role with confidence and a feeling that she could do anything she wanted, if she set her mind to it. And the first thing she did was buy her own car. Sure, her father was there to make sure she made a good decision; however, she wanted to assert her independence, so when he strongly suggested she buy a less expensive, but reliable, used car, she chose another direction. The financial representative and saleswoman had both told her she qualified to purchase a new car, and they assured her that it was a good decision. New cars came with warranties and were less likely to need costly repairs. That was enough to make the young service technician sign the papers to buy a fresh-off-the-line car with some fun bells and whistles.

When she was asked about the extras—an extended warranty, rustproofing, and undercoating—Emily said yes. After all, she was buying a new car and she wanted it to last. An hour later, though, when the papers were placed in front of her to transfer ownership and seal the deal, she did suffer a little sticker shock. With taxes, registration, and title transfer, the total cost was significantly higher than the sticker price. When her father reminded her that she had to pay for gasoline, insurance, and routine maintenance on top of her car payment, she felt a tinge of regret, though it was short-lived and pushed aside with the thrill of being a first-time car buyer and the confidence she gained in knowing that the process of study, practice, and apply works and she has that to fall back on.

Several months later, the thrill was replaced with worry. Sighing as she got into the car to go to work, she did the calculations—her payment was due in ten days. Once confident that she could easily afford to pay off the loan, even early, she now realized that money was tight, and she wished she'd taken her father's advice and bought something more affordable. Sure, she was working full time, and she loved her job, but when she bought the car, she was counting on additional income that just hadn't come to fruition.

She was aware of Champion's compensation program early on—team members were given opportunities to increase their income by performing well. Customer satisfaction was an important component, and so were sales. As a service technician, she made recommendations to clients, offering them upgrades and sometimes even new systems, which could avoid repair costs in aging systems. From day one, she vowed that this was one area where she would excel—and an area that would boost her income and help her build financial independence and stability very quickly.

By then, Emily was making service calls on her own. She had the knowledge to do her job and do it well. She knew the systems and the parts and upgrades that were available. As she'd been trained to do, she provided clients with the recommendations that were needed. For some reason, though, her clients weren't moving forward with her recommendations. To her disappointment, the paycheck that was once climbing was now stuck at base pay, with no additional compensation.

This recent lack of performance weighed heavily on Emily's mind. Was it because her clients didn't trust her? Did they think she lacked experience because she was young? She wasn't sure. Not only was she worried about being able to make her car payments, she was growing increasingly concerned that perhaps her mom and Brooke were right and she should have taken a different career path.

These thoughts stayed with her when she walked in Champion's doors. She was so preoccupied with them that Emily barely acknowledged her fellow team members. Her unusual quietness caught the attention of her supervisor, David.

It's time, David thought to himself. Keenly observant, David knew when something was bothering his team members, and to be honest, he'd been watching Emily. Her performance numbers were down, and he sensed something was bothering her. He had considered talking with her if she wasn't able to turn them around, and today he sensed that there was no need to delay.

"Good morning, Emily," he smiled. "Hey, I was hoping you could have lunch with me today—my treat. Meet me at noon at The Bay Café on North Street?"

After agreeing, Emily grabbed her schedule for the morning, quickly perusing the parts and supplies she'd need for the calls. Loading up her service van, she drove to her first call, mentally rehearsing the upgrades she'd recommend.

Four hours later, she was still depressed when she joined David for lunch. Once again, every client had declined her recommendations, leaving her confused and full of anxiety over her future.

David made small talk while they waited for their server to take their order, at least Emily thought he did. She could hear his voice, but she was pretending to listen; her mind was elsewhere, still wondering what she had been doing wrong and how she could turn it around with the clients she'd see that afternoon.

"Hello! Emily—calling Emily ... are you there?" David asked, snapping his fingers to get her attention.

"Huh? Oh, sorry. I guess my mind was somewhere else," Emily confessed.

"Is something bothering you, Emily?" her supervisor asked with genuine concern.

"Um, no ... well, I guess I just have some things on my mind," she admitted.

"Oh, I know how that goes. I used to be like that, too. Many times my wife and I would be at dinner together, and I'd be sitting right across the table, and mentally, I was somewhere else. I was always thinking about tomorrow and the next thing I had to take care of. Sometimes, I was focused on the past, what went wrong, and what I could have done differently. I was failing to be present and in the *now,* and my wife pointed it out to me. It was difficult for me to enjoy the meal and my time with my loved ones. Thankfully, I've since overcome that and live for the moment, which is truly all we can control. Do you agree, Emily?" he smiled.

"I'm sorry, David. I was thinking about my next call. I received the information and am just preparing for what might be wrong and what I'll need on the call. After all, my numbers are poor, and it's killing me."

"Look, I know about your numbers, and that's why I wanted to talk to you today. Emily, I've noticed that your truck revenue sales numbers are low, and your client satisfaction scores are slightly lower than our goal. I want to help you turn that around. In just these last few minutes, I can see one reason why you're struggling. When we meet with our clients, we need to be sure we are with that *one* client, and that one client *only.* That client is what we should be thinking about, versus the next one or even our performance numbers, for that matter. Being fully present and in the now and fully engaged to serve is all that matters."

"Yes," Emily agreed. "I have to pick up my numbers. What if I lose my job? I have an expensive car payment that I worry about, and …"

As she went on and on, David could feel her anxiety.

"I get it. The results you're so concerned about and whether you can pay your bills are things that are actually working against you. Let me give you an analogy in baseball. When a player is anxious about their batting average or they're in a hitting slump, they start gripping their bat too tight. When that happens, they'll never get a hit. And do you know what their coaches tell them? To get out of their own head and work from their heart. To remember their love for the game and go out there and have fun doing what they love to do. If you do that, your pocketbook will take care of itself. You just have to trust that. And by the way, working from the heart is where joy comes from—where the passion lives. It's when you're working from the heart, versus the head, that you can let it all go. And take my word for it, when you're stressed, clients can sense it and, in turn, it impacts them and their decisions."

"David, I just want to know what I'm doing wrong. I mean, I did so well at the university! I thought I'd be rocking it and doing great by now," Emily said in an exasperated tone.

"You might be thinking of this as a communication problem. Maybe you're fixated on the numbers and the technical side of your job. I would like to offer a third option, though, and state that I believe you might be going through a mindset problem. The toughest improvement to go through is self-improvement, and that's because it takes people completely out of their comfort zone," he said.

"I'm following you. You might be right. The thing is I want to know what to do about it."

"That's easy, Emily. Be present and in the now. Life is short. Life is precious. Be happy with what is going right. It's about connection and being present and in the *now*," he emphasized. You'll spend 8 to 10 and maybe 12 hours a day working, so enjoy it. My advice is to stop focusing on the past. Stop thinking about what you could have done differently yesterday or on your last service call. Instead, focus on today and making progress. Like our core value reads, focus on progress and measure backwards."

"Measure backwards? Can you explain that?" requested the service technician.

"Absolutely. Our minds are a beautiful gift that God has given us. The mind is a blessing, and it can be a curse if used in the wrong way. Our minds are goal-seeking devices; they want to accomplish and achieve things. It's amazing, which is why I called it beautiful," David smiled. "When you achieve something, let's say a goal, your mind automatically seeks to move to the next goal or achievement. That is the blessing. Now, the curse is determined by how we measure ourselves. Do we measure ourselves against the next goal that is constantly being moved out as we achieve more, or do we measure ourselves from where we came from and where we were? That's where the term 'measure backwards' comes from.

"Always measuring yourself against where you want to be, 'measuring forward,' creates anxiety. Measuring forward means worrying about those goals and where you want to be tomorrow. How am I going to get to where I want to be? It'll never happen. I can't do it. Those are negative, pessimistic thoughts. On the other hand, when you measure backwards, you see how far you've come, rather than how far you have to go. Emily, look how far you've come since you joined us at Champion!"

"I have, or so I thought," she replied.

"Focus on the progress you've made, Emily. Let go of perfection and measure backwards. That creates satisfaction, optimism, and happiness."

"I believe you, David. I also believe that might be easier said than done," Emily said.

"It takes a conscious effort, but it can be done. Remember that I was also guilty of forward thinking and worrying about the future. I overcame it by being grateful, and I found a way to make sure I integrate gratitude into my everyday mindset."

"How?" Emily asked, leaning forward in her chair.

"Every morning, I make it a point to write down my three or four wins from the previous day," David explained.

"What's a win?"

"A win is something that went right. I made someone smile. I had a great call with a client or a productive meeting with my team. It could be that I got to spend time doing something special with my kids. I enjoyed a leisurely walk or connected with a good friend. It could be achieving a goal, helping a stranger, or simply having a great hair day," he laughed. "Seriously, though, we all have wins in our life—we have something to be grateful for and people we care about."

"So, how does reviewing your wins help?"

"It's all about gratitude. What you appreciate, appreciates. You get more of what you're thankful for. So, if you focus on the things that went right, you can expect that more things will go right!"

"Really? Do you really think that will help me, David?" Emily asked her supervisor.

"I'm sure it will. It's one of our core values, and it's my favorite. It's a reminder that we all need to be grateful. At Champion, we are all about having an attitude of gratitude. Once you're grateful, you'll move right into the joy, where you'll be able to leave your stress and anxiety behind and truly live in the present, in the now. We can't change the past, so why worry about it? We cannot control the future, so why waste so much time thinking about it? The only thing that matters in life is what is going on right now. Free yourself and control the one thing that is in your power — the present and how you think about it. That's the Champion mindset, and it's a winning mindset. If you follow it, success will follow. You'll get more of what you're grateful for, and that's cause for joy, isn't it?"

"It sure is!" Emily agreed. "I think I've got a lot of lost time to make up for, David. So starting tomorrow morning, I'm going to write down my three wins for the previous day!"

"Glad to hear it, and I'm confident that it will make a difference in your life. I know it did in mine. And remember, I'm here to support you all the way. Here," he said, reaching down into his bag on the floor and handing her a black journal with gold letters embossed on its cover.

"What's this?" she asked.

"It's your Champion Mindset journal. Joe gave a talk on this core value last year and had a few hundred of them made. When I saw how preoccupied you were this morning, I had a hunch and grabbed one for you," he explained. "When you document your wins, you will be able to see that you are making progress. You have come far — you have learned so much. Sometimes, it might have felt like you were drinking water out of a fire hose. I know—I've been there. I want you to realize, though, that it is nearly impossible to replicate what you learned while in our university. There are too many factors that are beyond your control when you walk into someone else's home and their environment. Naturally, it will be different, and you might have different results. Guess what, though? That's okay. We are all imperfect, and if we make the mistake of expecting perfection, we will always be disappointed."

"Thank you! I really appreciate your support … and this journal, David. I promise to give it a try—*no,* I'm not going to give it a try. I'm going to do it! Starting tomorrow morning, I'm going to write down my wins."

"Remember, Emily, that it's a two-step process. The first step is looking back, and the second step is being creative and looking forward," he explained. "You have to be intentional to do this, and I warn you it might feel uncomfortable or awkward at first. As you become familiar with the process, it will start to feel natural. Eventually, it will become a habit for you, like it has for me."

"That makes so much sense, David!" Emily exclaimed. "And it seems like something I can really do!"

"The key is to allow yourself to enjoy the process. Have fun with it. Life is short. Enjoy it. We owe it to ourselves to do that," David said. "It's easy to do, and easier not to do."

"I will. Starting this afternoon, I'm going to go on every call with that attitude. I *do* love my job … I guess I just got consumed with worry about bills, money, and the numbers."

"I understand; I did the same thing. Live for and enjoy the moment. Be in the present and have fun, and then be grateful for each moment. When you do—"

"I'll have even more to be grateful for!" Emily interjected, finishing her manager's sentence for him.

"Sounds like a Champion mindset to me," David laughed. "Clients can sense when you're uncertain or feeling self-doubt, and you transfer that uncertainty to them. The good news is that they will also sense confidence and positivity, and that will provide them with the assurance that you have only their best interests at heart. They'll know that the recommendations you are making are for *them,* not for you. The journal that you hold in your hand is the tool that will give you that confidence and the gratitude that creates the attitude that produces the results you *want.* Do you follow me?"

"I do. And I trust that *you* have my best interests at heart. I already know the first 'win' I'm going to write in my journal," she replied.

"What's that?"

"I had a productive meeting with a very supportive supervisor today!" proclaimed Emily.

"That sounds like an excellent start. I think my work here is done. And look, we still have a little time—let's enjoy the moment … and our lunch!"

8

BE KIND AND ENCOURAGING

We genuinely care for others and their overall well-being.
We are great listeners, and we use words
to inspire and build people up.

 True to her word, Emily committed to writing her wins in her journal every morning. As she continued the practice, she found it gave her confidence when she reflected on all that she'd accomplished from the previous day. In addition to her win about a great meeting with her supervisor, David, she also wrote a few more:

I met with some great clients yesterday—the Jones'—on my first call. I took the time to learn about their family in Minnesota and all the lakes they went to when growing up. It was a great connection. I was really aware of listening versus speaking. Built a ton of trust. I got them happily involved in our maintenance program. Excited to see them on our next regular service.

I worked out this morning for 45 minutes. Loved it! I got a great sweat on! I'm proud of myself. I'm delighted that I've stayed committed to my Monday, Wednesday, Friday routine.

I called my cousin, Brian, last night. Great call, great connection. I love that guy! I'm thankful, Lord, for connections made even 3,000 miles away.

Set up my autopay for my bills. Such a relief. So thankful to get that off my mind.

There were days when Emily woke up a bit groggy and her attitude was less than stellar. As soon as she picked up her pen and wrote her wins from the previous day, she noticed that the "stinkin' thinkin'" was gone.

Just as David said, reflecting on her wins really did give her confidence. It also got her excited for the day to come. Setting goals became a daily habit, and it was easy to do because she felt great. What a difference a change of attitude makes.

David told Emily that this daily mind exercise would allow her to capitalize on the day to come, and she was quickly discovering that he was so right. She could hear his words in her mind: "Momentum plays such a huge factor in life. Think of a football team at the end of the game. As they start moving down the field completing passes, one after another after another, the momentum is high, and it's a real thing. The same is true with your goal setting, Emily. The time to do it is when you've just written your accomplishments. It's using that momentum to propel you forward for what you want to achieve today. Your achievements yesterday will give you the raw material for what you want to accomplish today."

Emily thought about David's words and once she finished writing her accomplishments, she quickly wrote down her goals or wins for today:

WINS FOR TODAY:

1. Use at least three of the open-ended questions on the pocket coach on each call today.
2. Call Jen and see if she wants to join me in workouts as my regular partner.
3. Call my mom today and be sure to listen and hear what's going on in her life. Serve her.

As Emily finished writing her wins, she realized how connected her wins for today were to her accomplishments from yesterday. She had an aha moment and saw the power of momentum right before her eyes.

Just as David said would happen, the results followed, and she told him so.

"David, I just wanted to say thank you! I really appreciate the advice you gave me, and you were right, it's making a difference," she said.

"I've been wanting to talk to you, too, Emily. I'm happy that you're seeing results, but let's back up. Have you paid attention to your customer satisfaction scores lately? Really paid attention? You've been on an impressive and consistent upward trend since we had our lunch. I'm proud of you!" he said.

"Thank you. Writing in my journal has helped me a lot. If you have a minute, I'd like to share something else that I think has made a big difference in my outcomes," she said.

"I always love to hear wins! Have a seat—I'm all ears," her supervisor welcomed.

"Well, what I've been applying besides the journal is right there on the wall," she said, pointing to a poster of the core values. "It's core value number six—be kind and encouraging. And let me tell you, it's been transformational for me!"

"Tell me about it," David said, leaning forward in his chair.

"Where do I start? Well, when I was training, I rode with a guy named Sam, and I saw him live this core value incredibly well. He truly took an interest in his clients, and I knew it worked because I saw his client satisfaction and revenue numbers. He impressed me so much that I wanted to model him in my interactions with clients."

"You're right, Sam epitomizes this core value and represents kindness and encouragement with everyone he encounters. He's an incredible role model for core value number six. I do want to point out that I love something you just said, Emily, when you said you wanted to model him. That's what we teach in Champion's core value number four—to be a lifelong student and learn from the successes of others," David said, voicing his approval.

"Just that one day with Sam taught me so much. Following Sam's example, I am genuinely taking a deep care and interest in our clients, just like the core value states. I look to put myself in their shoes and really see things from their perspective. Along the same line, I've studied empathy—remember, you told us in our training meetings that we need to have empathy? Well, I've incorporated it in my relationships with clients and strive to see things from their perspective, versus my perspective. Even more, I'm finding that I spend so much more time listening to what the client is really saying and finding out what their true needs are. I've found that's so much more effective than presuming I know what their needs are! Before, I was doing most of the talking, telling clients what *I* was doing and focusing on me and the results that *I* wanted. By learning more about this core value, I've discovered that I need to listen. In addition, I've discovered something even more profound."

"What's that?" her supervisor asked.

"As I focused on the word 'listen,' I came to the realization that the very same letters, when placed in a different order, spell the word 'silent.' It dawned on me that in order to listen, I have to be silent, so I can really hear what clients are telling me. That blew me away, and it's made a world of difference. I'm sure it's why I've become better and better at asking great open-ended questions."

"Silent – I love that, Emily! I'm sure it will benefit you in all of your relationships—that's another win," David remarked. "We've spent 12 years, some of us 16 years, of our lives in school learning how to read, write, and speak. These are important communication skills, yes. How much time and how many classes did any of us attend on the most important communication skill, which is listening? The answer is likely, none. It is imperative that we become great listeners and, more so, active listeners. Most people listen with the intent to respond, rather than with the intent to understand. Let me give you an example:

"Let's say you're out at a restaurant and you look over at the table next to you, and there are four people seated around it. One person begins to share a story about their daughter who made the volleyball team at school, and immediately someone else shares something about their son or daughter and what they've accomplished or achieved. The third person then shares something similar that's been triggered in their mind with all the conversation flowing. Then finally, the fourth person chimes in, and they're doing the same thing, which is running their mouth, listening with the intent to respond. This is what I call one-upmanship."

"Oh, I've heard conversations like that! You're right—they are one-upping each other!"

"They sure are. What we teach our team to do is to listen with the intent to understand. Enjoy the story, learn from it, show that you care, even reflect what was shared to let the person know you heard them. When you do this, you're serving the person sharing the story. You're allowing them to sit in the big chair, while you're quite content to sit in the small chair. This is active listening—a forgotten skill in our 'what about me' society. What we believe is in order to stand out in today's world, do the opposite of what the crowd is doing and become an active listener. Leaders are active listeners, and they're okay with the spotlight being shined on someone else."

"Wow, David, that is such good insight and so in line with core value number six."

"Yes, it is, Emily. It's almost like communication jujitsu—using an apparent weakness, listening and allowing others to shine, and turning it into an actual strength. One other thing that's kind of ironic is that, when you put this active listening into use, you'll become known as a great conversationalist by others, even though in most cases, you'll be speaking 20 percent of the time and allowing others to speak 80 percent."

"Again, David, I'm blown away! The concept works, and I've witnessed the results firsthand. Now, when I *do* speak, I keep it positive, just like it says in the core value. I use my words to inspire, encourage, and lift the client up. I tell them what is working right with their home comfort system, versus just telling them what's wrong. In the end, the conversation is so much more enjoyable and positive. The greatest thing, David, is I am in control of that. Even when the conversation starts to take a negative turn, I can shift it back to the positive!"

"I'd love an example," David encouraged.

"Okay, just yesterday, I was at a client's house, and I commented on how beautiful the blue Tesla in their driveway was. Right away, the client came back with a negative comment, saying that he can only drive it for 200 miles before it needs to be recharged. I immediately noticed that the conversation had taken a shift toward the negative, so I said something along the lines about how great it is that we're seeing more and more new charging stations being installed every day. David, I could see it in his eyes—I had given him a compliment, and he unintentionally was looking to deflect it and bring up something negative. I took back control of the conversation by finding something positive regarding the charging stations, and a realization came to him that, yeah, there are more stations going in. This kept it positive," Emily explained.

"Way to go, Emily! That was quick thinking, and you're right. They do seem to be popping up everywhere," her supervisor said.

"I realized that keeping the conversation positive is my responsibility and I am in control of that. Realizing that was so refreshing, and I've started practicing it in all areas of my life. It even helped when my uncle and I had another one of our little disagreements," she said. "Even though we don't always see eye to eye, we kept our remarks positive, and we both walked away feeling heard and respected."

"That's great. Actually, I was going to explain this core value to you today. It's obvious, though, that you've got this core value down. Your explanation knocked it out of the park!"

"Thank you. I owe everything I've learned to you, Joe, and people like Sam," she said.

"The best thing about this core value, Emily, is that takes less effort to be kind and encouraging than it does to be otherwise," David pointed out.

"I guess you're right. It's like it takes fewer muscles to smile than to frown …"

"You've got it. Being kind and encouraging to others is free. It takes more thought than effort. I can tell you that it'll make a faster and more impressive impact on your career and your relationships than almost anything else you can do."

"You really think so?" asked Emily.

"It's what my mentor told me," David told her.

"Oh, who is your mentor?"

"Joe, the owner of our company. He's the greatest leader I've had the privilege of knowing. Joe created the principles, philosophies, and core values we live and work by. Long ago, he became very skilled at identifying people who had what it takes to successfully apply them," advised David.

"How does he do it?" Emily asked.

"Let's just say that over time, you learn to recognize that there are champions within people. Our job is to help them recognize that they are champions, and the core values were specifically created to do that," David said.

"That said, I'm glad we had this talk today, and I'm pleased with your progress. When you first walked through our doors, Joe predicted that you would do well here. Once again, he was right."

"How could he know? I had no experience," Emily began …

"A champion doesn't need experience, Emily. We can give anyone experience. What a real champion needs is the right mindset and the core values that show them how to use it. Today, you showed me that you are a champion. It will be interesting to see where that takes you, Emily," David said as he rose from his chair. "Now I think it's time to call it a day. Let's go see if we can spread some of that kindness and encouragement with the rest of the world."

9

ALWAYS MAKE YOUR FUTURE BIGGER THAN YOUR PAST

Looking around the meeting room, Emily reflected on her career.

At the beginning, she'd been introduced to the career path of a service technician. Champion had created a career path for every position within the company, showing the job duties, expectations, requirements, and pay ranges for each one. There were six levels on the service technician career path. When she was hired, she started at the beginning of the path as a training level technician. She'd learned a lot since then; Champions University had taught her so much, other technicians had provided her with on-the-job experience and guidance, and mentors like Joe and David had shared their wisdom, insights, and experiences every step of the way.

Sure, there had been struggles, as there often are. Emily was grateful that she had been able to overcome them, again thanks to the advice and support she'd received from her mentors and fellow team members.

During the process, she became good at her job, so good that it became evident to her that achieving the next level on the Service Technician career path was well within her reach. Knowing that, she had something to work for. She just had to make sure she remembered the process and applied the core values. According to Joe and David, that was how to succeed. Living the company culture was her competitive advantage.

And it worked! Emily noticed a steady upward trend in her client satisfaction scores and her monthly revenue. She was meeting all of the expectations of a training technician on a consistent basis. It felt to her like she was rocking it, and she felt like she could take on anything.

When Joe and David informed her that she was being promoted to a maintenance technician, she felt like she was on top of the world. It was quite an accomplishment, and the reward brought her more than pride—it came with a respectable increase in pay. While she had managed to pay her car off early, she was now working on saving enough for a down payment on her first house—another milestone that she was striving to achieve.

And she'd done it all while her former classmates were still living in dorms and cramming for mid-terms and final exams. It had only taken her a couple months to attend Champions University and less than two years on the job to receive her first promotion. And that felt amazing.

I've put in so much time and energy in making it to this level. It's so great to be able to sit back and relax for a bit, she thought.

So she took a deep breath and enjoyed an opportunity to slow down and be proud of what she'd done.

No one was more surprised than she was to discover that her revenues were dropping after her promotion, and that realization transformed her pride to discouragement.

When David walked into the meeting room, she told him so.

"It's almost like I'm starting over. David, it's so discouraging. Why is this happening again?" she asked, remembering when she faced similar struggles as a training technician.

"Emily, the reason we created this career path is to give people a clear path and vision on how they can continue to grow and achieve in their journey here at Champion Air Conditioning. Note the key word here is to *continue* to grow," he said. "Achieving a promotion was fantastic, and it should be celebrated, Emily, but keep in mind, it's just the beginning of your career.

"You started at the first level, as a Training Technician, and now you're on level two and a Maintenance Technician. I commend you for that accomplishment. Each accomplishment, though, marks a new beginning, a new quest, and it should ignite a journey to the next level. I've been through many levels on my own career path. At each level, the expectations, duties, and requirements got higher. Even so, I followed the career path precisely as it was written, and I rose to the top. I did it by adopting the mindset of a champion and the culture of our company."

"Will you help me figure out why I'm falling short of expectations, David?" Emily plead.

"Absolutely. I want you to remember that you've successfully overcome similar challenges in the past. It's normal to face growth pains along the way. We all have. I know I certainly have. Still, I made it through all of these different levels of Service Technicians, and now that I'm a Service Manager, I'm thinking about what I have to do to become a General Manager."

"Really, David? That's an entirely different career path! You'll be starting all over!" Emily exclaimed.

"I know. When I became a Service Manager, it was short of my pinnacle. Sure, I could stop there, if I wanted to. If I did, I'd have reached the height of my career, and there's nowhere to go from there. I want to continue to grow, learn, and improve. It gives me something to work toward and look forward to. If I'd already reached my pinnacle, there would be nothing to look forward to. I want to have something to work toward, something to get excited about. Don't you?"

"Sure, I do. But what if I fail this time?" she asked.

"Good question. You've got to be careful because success breeds failure. And when you've had success, it can easily cause you to fall into struggle, unless you have the mindset of always making your future bigger than your past," David explained.

"Making my future bigger than my past?"

"Yes. The way to make your future bigger than your past is to remember that you have to be whether-driven—it will depend on whether you have the right mindset and whether you follow the Champion process in the different steps on your journey," he said.

"How do I know the right process to follow and steps to take this time?"

"That's easy. It's all laid out there in your career path. You know what you have to do, and the core values were designed specifically to help you do it and do it very well. Yes, you might fall short from time to time. And that's okay as long as you learn from it and appreciate the progress you *have* made. No matter what you accomplish, be satisfied with it and be thankful for it. Appreciate it, and let it spur you forward, versus holding you back," her supervisor advised.

"Do you think I can really do it, David? Do you think I have what it takes to rise through all six levels of my career path?" asked Emily.

"Of course, I do. And do you know how I know?" he asked.

"No," Emily answered honestly.

"Because you're a champion. You have a champion mindset. I've watched you grow and achieve so much since you joined our family, and I'm excited to see just how big that future will be, Emily."

* * * *

Several years later, Emily was sitting at the same table when Joe walked by. However, the tables had turned. This time, she was the mentor and the person across from her was a training technician. Joe paused when he heard Emily explaining to the young man the Service Technician career path and helping him understand that it was his pathway to advancement and success.

"How long does it take to achieve all six levels?" he asked.

"That's up to you. You do have expectations and requirements in each level, and moving up will depend on your initiative," she explained. "You can accelerate the process, or you can take it slow and steady. The most important thing is to make each day a little better than the day before. When you have something to strive for and you make progress, even a little at a time, you'll always make your future bigger than your past. That's what we all want here at Champion, for you, for our company, and for our clients."

"I appreciate that," the young man said.

"Now, here is a copy of our core values," she said, handing him a small, laminated version of the core values that were posted on the wall behind her. "As time goes on, you will learn and live them in your career here. I've found it's helpful to carry them on me, especially at the beginning, when they were new to me."

"Okay, thanks. And these will help me?" he asked.

"Our core values are the culture of our company. They were specifically created to be Champion's competitive advantage. If you use them consistently, they can be your competitive advantage, too," she said. "Those core values helped me on my career path, so I know they work."

"How do they work?" the training technician asked.

"They build a Champion Mindset, and when you have that, you'll always make your future bigger than your past," Emily said as she noticed Joe standing just outside the doorway. Catching her eye, he smiled in approval. Since the first day she'd walked through their doors, she'd come a long way. And now she was taking it upon herself to pay it forward and pass on what she'd learned.

Joe gave her a thumbs up and proceeded down the hallway. As he neared his office, he knew the new recruit was in good hands— Emily had become a true Champion, and that was something they could both be proud of.

10

THE REAL STORY

 I have faith you enjoyed reading *Champion Mindset*. Moreover, it is my sincere wish that this story instilled in you the philosophy and core values that have been the foundation of my real-life company, Service Champions in Northern California. Whether you are a new recruit, an existing team member, a client, or a small business owner, this story reveals that the only competitive advantage any company has in the marketplace is their culture.

While this story is fictional, the philosophies and values shared in it are very real. They have paved the way to success on my career path since Service Champions was founded.

In 2003, when I started my company, I gathered the original team members together and asked this question: "When they write the book about Service Champions, what do we want to be remembered for?" That question spawned the making of our core values and how we wanted to be remembered. Years later, I'm delighted to share them in this book that tells the story of our core values and our company culture. Although the company name and characters used in the book are make-believe, what is real is close to 20 years of excellent performance and team members who have excelled and grown both personally and professionally.

This was by design. You see, developing people is my passion in life, and I started my business with this concept in mind. I never had a real passion for heating and air conditioning when I was growing up. What I saw was a trade that gave me a vehicle to grow and train people to be more than what they thought was possible. I learned at an early age from the great Zig Ziglar that the way you get everything you want in life is to help as many people as you can get what they want. That has been my mission with Service Champions from the start.

I wanted to influence a lot of people, so that meant I needed to build a large company. I wanted my influence to extend beyond the walls of Service Champions, so I knew I needed to be an industry leader.

I was unemployed for six months leading up to the day I started Service Champions. In that period of time, I created a detailed plan of a multi-location residential heating and air conditioning business. I was specific with numbers I wanted to grow to, $50 million in revenue. There was no other company in our industry that had ever achieved that. We came out of the gate and had explosive growth. We grew to $15 million in revenue annually within our fourth year of business. Yes, the accolades and recognition across the country began to roll in. I was achieving the goal that I set out with, which was to influence a large number of people inside the company and around the United States.

What we learned over the next several years was that success is messy. We were building a great company, and, at the same time, we were faced with challenges that would test me and the other leaders inside the organization. We had unfounded class action lawsuits, over a million-dollar embezzlement, and some major cash flow challenges. Through it all, our team stayed resilient and true to our philosophy and core values. We continued on and persevered toward our $50-million-dollar goal.

As 2020 approached, the $50-million target was in our sights, so too were private equity who salivated over our business and culture and wanted to partner with us to take us to the next level. Right in the middle of the pandemic, we were approached by a well-known private equity firm, Leonard Green Partners (LGP). I had a friend I'd known for years, Ken Haines, who was the CEO of the HVAC company owned by LGP, the Wrench Group. Ken and I worked on a deal for several months that would be life-changing for my family and so many others inside the company. I worked with an investment banking firm out of Los Angeles named Intrepid. The lead banker on our deal was Jeremiah Mann. He helped guide the entire process and was a true pro.

On July 1, 2020, the deal was finalized, and the Wrench Group and Leonard Green Partners have lived up to every promise they made prior to the transaction. They told me they wanted me to continue to run the business as an entrepreneur and owner-operator—that was easy because I still have a significant ownership stake in the business.

They also told me they loved our culture and our core values and they wanted them to continue to drive the success of our business.

Well, that is exactly what they have done. Building a $50-million company was my vision and goal from the beginning. The amazing part is, as of June 30, 2020, our financials for a 12-month period showed $50 million in revenue for the very first time. We had hit our "Big Hairy Audacious Goal" that I set prior to starting the company on the day I sold the business. You can't make this stuff up!

Since the deal, we've enjoyed explosive growth, and I'm certain it's because our culture, core values, and philosophy are at work. They have and will continue to spur Service Champions to increased growth and success. Today, we're in year two with the new owners, and we achieved over $75 million in revenue.

It took us 17 years to achieve $50 million in revenue. It will only take us 4 years to add an additional $50 million, making us a $100-million company.

What I've learned is that culture is the only competitive advantage a company has in the marketplace. There are many HVAC businesses out there that can fix air conditioners and furnaces, and we know that. Having a culture that is supported by a clear set of core values and team members who have the right mindset and philosophy has made all the difference. I want to thank all of the champions at Service Champions for building such a beautiful company. The exciting part is we're just getting started, and there's so much growth and opportunity to look forward to.

Here's to a bigger future,

Kevin Comerford

11

TOP TAKE-AWAYS
FROM EACH CHAPTER

In this final chapter, I share the top take-aways from the main chapters of the book (Chapters 1-9). I've done this for the person who wants a condensed version of the "nuggets" that Champion Mindset has to offer. Enjoy!

Chapter 1 – The First Day

1) Great leaders go out daily and visit their people. They use a technique called MBWA (Management by Walking Around).

2) Be great at asking questions to your people. Show them that you care and are interested in them. Be present with them and be a great listener. This is what it takes to be a CEO.

3) Being honest and authentic sets you free as a leader. Your stress levels will decrease significantly when you tell the truth.

Chapter 2 – Whether-Driven

1) Whether-driven is the core philosophy of our company. Your

success depends on WHETHER you come to work with the right attitude and WHETHER you follow the Champion process.

2) Have an abundancy mindset, which means there is plenty for all of us and you will always be taken care of. People with an abundancy mindset are grateful for what they have or know. An abundancy mindset leaves you feeling excited, motivated, and energized for action.

3) A scarcity mindset is the opposite of abundance. People with a scarcity mindset believe that everything necessary for future progress is becoming scarce and running out. Scarcity is driven by fear and leaves you feeling overwhelmed, depressed, and paralyzed.

Chapter 3 – Give Remarkable Service

1) Every core value starts with a verb or an action word. They are designed to be the behaviors and the way we act with our clients and fellow team members.

2) The definition of Service: Taking action to create value for someone else.

3) Be aware of the wake you leave behind after every interaction. Is it positive and uplifting, or negative?

Chapter 4 – Drive Top Performance

1) We are a meritocracy: Your compensation is in direct proportion to your contribution. If you want to earn more, contribute more.

2) It's important to balance driving sales with client satisfaction scores. They are equally important.

3) All great performers love to be held accountable. It drives them and makes them better.

Bonus:

4) Great performers "know thy numbers." They always know where they stand against their goal, and they use that information to drive them into action.

Chapter 5 – Honor Your Commitments

1) When you have a client challenge, own up to it and give the client the feeling that you're running toward them.

2) The number one way to build trust in any relationship is to follow through with what you say you're going to do.

3) Be careful when making commitments and saying "yes" all the time. When you're unable to honor those commitments, it chips away at your self-esteem and confidence.

Chapter 6 – Be a Lifelong Student

1) We are a people-development company. The only way to make your company better is to make the people inside your company better.

2) Learning is a gift you give yourself for life. It is a never-ending process, and you are responsible.

3) Leaders are readers. Build this continuous habit to work on yourself. If you want to make a living, work hard at your job; if you want to make a fortune, work hard on yourself.

Chapter 7 – Have Fun and Enjoy the Moment

1) Being fully present with the person you are with is most important in your personal and business life.

2) If you work from your heart, rather than from your head, you will enjoy yourself so much more. The client can tell the difference, and it impacts their decisions.

3) Measure backwards. This is a key attribute to happiness and satisfaction. Always measure where you came from versus measuring yourself against some future goal. Focus on progress, rather than perfection.

Chapter 8 – Be Kind and Encouraging

1) Listen with the intent to understand versus listening with the intent to respond.

2) If you change the order of the letters in the word "listen," it magically spells out "silent." Practice letting others sit in the big chair, while you sit in the small chair.

3) It is your responsibility as a leader to keep the conversation positive. Use your words to inspire, encourage, and lift others.

Chapter 9 – Always Make Your Future Bigger Than Your Past

1) Success breeds failure. When you've had success, it can cause you to fall into struggle, unless you have the personal philosophy of always making your future bigger than your past. Have a beginner's mind.

2) No matter what you accomplish, be satisfied with it and thankful for it. What you appreciate, appreciates.

3) Always give back and pay it forward. You are honoring all of those people who taught and trained you.

ABOUT KEVIN COMERFORD

Kevin Comerford is a successful entrepreneur who built a highly profitable $75-million home services business, with 315 team members in Northern California. He is on the way to $125 million and over 500 team members within the next three years. With the help of great mentors and a great team at Service Champions, Kevin created a unique culture in the business where team members grow both personally and professionally. He lives in Pleasanton, California, with his beautiful wife, Carolyn, and their three children, Emily, Brendan, and Landon.

To maximize your Champion Mindset experience, we invite you to visit www.Kevincomerford.net, where you can receive additional resources and insights.

Made in the USA
Coppell, TX
09 February 2023

12562310R00075